KS2 Success

LEARN AND PRACTISE

Maths and English

Paul Broadbent & Alison Head

Contents

MATHS

Using and applying mathematics

Counting and understanding numbers

Knowing and using number facts

Calculating

Understanding shape

Measuring

Handling data

Glossary

Contents

ENGLISH

Speaking and listening

Reading

Writing

Glossary

Maths and English Answers

Word problems

Answering problems

If you have a word problem to solve, try using these four stages.

A bag costs £6.80. What change would there be from a ten-pound note?

1   Read the problem. Try to picture the problem and imagine going through it in real life.
2   Sort out the calculations. Find the difference by counting on from £6.80 to £10.
3   Answer the calculations. £10.00 – £6.80 is £3.20.
4   Answer the problem. Look back at the question – what is it asking?

The change from a ten-pound note for the bag is £3.20.

Multi-step problems

Word problems can have different numbers of calculations to answer before you reach the final answer.

One-step problems
There are 185 boys and 217 girls in a school.
What is the total number of children?

$185 + 217 = 402$ 402 children in total.

Two-step problems
900g of flour and 500g of sugar are mixed together and then divided equally into two bowls. What is the weight of the mixture in each bowl?

Step 1
$900g + 500g = 1400g$

Step 2
$1400 ÷ 2 = 700g$

So there is 700g of mixture in each bowl.

Key words   difference   total

Answering problems

1 There are 270g of cake mixture in a bowl. It is divided equally between 9 bun cases. What is the weight of the mixture in each case? ☐ g

2 Robert is one-fifth of his mother's age. If his mother is 35, how old is Robert? ☐

3 From Leeds, it is 81km to Manchester and 62km to York. How much further is it from Leeds to Manchester than to York? ☐ km

4 A hall has 265 chairs in total. At a concert all but 25 chairs are used. How many people are at the concert? ☐

5 A bike costs £136 and a helmet costs £35. How much do they cost altogether? £ ☐

6 A regular hexagon has 6 equal sides. Each side is 9cm in length. What is the distance around the whole hexagon? ☐ cm

6

Multi-step problems

1 There are 4 weeks and 5 days until Rebecca's birthday. How many days is it in total until her birthday? _____

2 Sam picks 58 apples and Ryan picks 62 apples. They put them together and then divide them equally between 6 bags. How many apples are in each bag? _____

3 Claire has 43 sweets to put into 9 party bags for her friends. How many will there be in each bag and how many will be left over? _____

4 Mr Benson posts 3 parcels. Two of the parcels cost £3.20 each and the other parcel costs £2.35. What is the total cost of posting the three parcels? _____

4

TOTAL MARKS ☐ 10

Problem-solving

Reasoning

If you need to think carefully about a way to solve a problem, you are likely to be using reasoning skills to make sense of it. It may help to explain the problem to someone else, describing the way you could try to solve it.

What colour is each shape?

Clues:
- there are three colours used
- yellow is not next to green
- the red square is next to the circle
- the green square is between two red shapes
- the squares are not yellow.

To answer questions like this, draw the shapes and find the clues that give the most help. The third clue shows that the first square is red. That means that the second square is green and the triangle is red. The circle must be yellow.

Always check each clue with your answer to make sure it is correct.

Finding all possibilities

These types of problems often have lots of different choices of answer and the skill is finding the correct one. You need to work systematically, making lists of all the possible answers to find the right one.

Find three consecutive numbers that add up to 39.

1 Trial and improvement method:

$14 + 15 + 16 = 45$.

It must be less:

$12 + 13 + 14 = 39$.

2 Using reasoning:

$39 \div 3 = 13$.

This must be the middle number:

$12 + 13 + 14 = 39$.

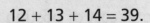

| Key words | consecutive |

Reasoning

1 Tom is 9 years old. His father is 36 years old. How many years older is Tom's father? Circle which of these you could use to work this out.

> 36 + 9   45 − 9   45 − 34   36 − 9   36 × 9   36 ÷ 9

2 I am thinking of a number. If I double it, the answer is 34. If I subtract 6 from it, the answer is 11. What number am I thinking of?

3 Zoe has some sweets in a box. She takes 5 out and then divides the rest equally into two bags. There are 14 sweets in each bag. How many sweets did she have in the box?

4 Use the clues to work out the colour of each shape.

Clues:
- green is between two reds
- the yellow circle is below a square
- blue is below green
- orange is on the right of blue.

4

Finding all possibilities

1 Three children ate a total of 29 grapes. Each of them ate a different odd number of grapes. If one of them ate 13 grapes, what possible numbers of grapes did the other two eat? _____

2 Fred bought some burgers and hot-dogs for his friends. Hot-dogs were 50p and burgers were 80p. He spent £6 in total, with 1 more burger than hot-dog bought. How many of each did he buy? _____

3 Alex spent £2 on 10p and 20p stickers. He bought three times as many 10p stickers as 20p stickers. How many of each sticker did he buy? _____

3

TOTAL MARKS 7

Rules and patterns

Number sequences

A sequence is a list of numbers written in order.

7　8　9　10　11　　　　　43　42　41　40　39

If you need to find missing numbers in a sequence, look carefully at the numbers you are given. Try to work out the numbers next to these first, then write the others.

127　128　____　____　131　____

So in this sequence, 129 follows 128, then the next number is 130. Which number follows 131?

Number patterns

Counting patterns can have numbers in different steps.
To work out the steps, look at the difference between the numbers.
Look at this counting pattern.

34　37　40　43　____

This is going up in threes. The next number is 46.

Top Tip
To help you work out the missing number, draw 'jumps' between each number and write the differences.

Function machines

You may have questions which ask you to find the numbers going in and coming out of a function machine.

If you are asked which number goes into the machine, you will need to know the inverse or opposite of the function.

6 → IN ×4 OUT → 24

The opposite of adding is subtracting.
The opposite of multiplying is dividing.

Key words　　　　　sequence　　inverse

Number sequences

Write the missing numbers in each sequence.

1 47 48 [   ] [   ] 51 52 [   ]

2 163 [   ] 165 [   ] 167 [   ] 169

3 [   ] [   ] 79 78 [   ] 76 75

4 297 298 299 [   ] [   ] [   ] 303

5 402 401 [   ] [   ] 398 397 [   ]

5

Number patterns

Continue these sequences in both directions.

1 [   ] [   ] 51 57 63 [   ] [   ]

2 [   ] [   ] 32 39 46 [   ] [   ]

3 [   ] [   ] 40 36 32 [   ] [   ]

4 [   ] [   ] 81 86 91 [   ] [   ]

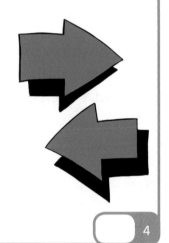

4

Function machines

Write the numbers coming out of these function machines.

1 49 → IN ÷7 OUT → [   ]

2 32 → IN +25 OUT → [   ]

Write the numbers going into these function machines.

3 [   ] → IN −9 OUT → 24

4 [   ] → IN ×8 OUT → 56

4

TOTAL MARKS 13

Place value and decimals

4-digit numbers

Look at these numbers and how they are made.

1572   one thousand five hundred and seventy-two

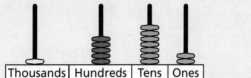 

7125   seven thousand one hundred and twenty-five

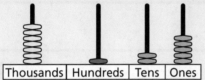 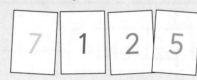

The position of a digit in a number is really important. 1572 and 7125 use the same digits, but they are very different numbers. Always check where you put each digit when you write numbers.

Decimal numbers

Decimal numbers are whole numbers divided into tenths and hundredths. A decimal point is used to separate whole numbers from decimals. Look at these number lines.

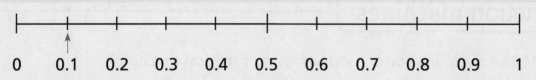

This shows tenths. 0.1 is the same as $\frac{1}{10}$.

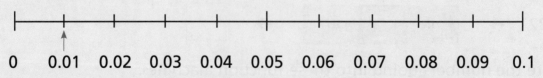

This shows hundredths. 0.01 is the same as $\frac{1}{100}$.

 Key words   digit

12

4-digit numbers

Write these number words as numerals.

1 nine thousand six hundred and forty-two

2 four hundred and twenty-five

3 three thousand two hundred and thirteen

4 one thousand five hundred and ninety-eight

5 six thousand and seventy

6 two thousand and fifty-eight

7 eight thousand three hundred and sixty

8 seven thousand and nine

8

Decimal numbers

Write the missing numbers in the boxes on these number lines.

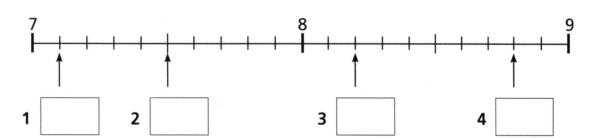

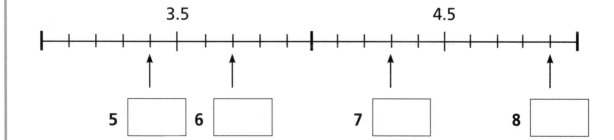

8

TOTAL MARKS   16

Comparing numbers

Comparing numbers

< and > are really useful symbols ... but don't get them confused!

< means 'is less than'   45 < 59   45 is less than 59.

> means 'is greater than'   142 > 124   142 is greater than 124.

When you need to compare two numbers, you must look carefully at the value of the digits.

Which is bigger, 87 or 78?

87 is the same as 80 + 7,

78 is the same as 70 + 8,

So 87 is bigger than 78.

Ordering numbers

If you have a list of numbers to put in order, it is a good idea to put the numbers into groups with the same number of digits.

For each group, arrange them in order of size, depending on the place value of the digits.

1   Put these in order, starting with the smallest.

600   3110   305   3200   529   1008   2945

2   Group the hundreds, then the thousands and put them in order.

600   305   529   →   305   529   600

3110   3200   1008   2945   →   1008   2945   3110   3200

3   Put them all together in order.

305   529   600   1008   2945   3110   3200

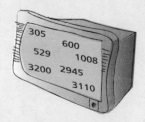

14

Comparing numbers

Write the correct < or > sign in each box.

1 56 ☐ 93

2 87 ☐ 78

3 44 ☐ 42

4 19 ☐ 61

5 53 ☐ 35

6 220 ☐ 310

7 964 ☐ 938

8 572 ☐ 575

9 414 ☐ 141

10 883 ☐ 838

10

Ordering numbers

Write each set of numbers in order of size, starting with the smallest.

smallest   largest

1 385   198   296   258   ☐ ☐ ☐ ☐

2 597   527   592   572   ☐ ☐ ☐ ☐

3 1043   4130   3014   4301   ☐ ☐ ☐ ☐

4 2665   2556   2656   2566   ☐ ☐ ☐ ☐

5 712   294   367   248   ☐ ☐ ☐ ☐

6 399   3939   393   9339   ☐ ☐ ☐ ☐

6

TOTAL MARKS ☐ 16

Estimating

Rounding

Rounding a number to the nearest ten is useful for estimating.
A 'round number' is a number ending in zero, such as 10, 20, 30, 40, 50, 60, 70, 80, 90 or 100.

Rounding is easy if you follow these two simple rules.

To round to the nearest 10, look at the 'ones' digit. Then …
1   If it is 5 or more, round up the tens digit.
2   If it is less than 5, the tens digit stays the same.

> So 84 rounds down to 80.
>
> 137 rounds up to 140.
>
> 265 rounds up to 270.

Half-way numbers ending in 5, such as 165, 145 and 385, always round up to the next ten.

 Remember, a number is always between two possible 'round' numbers – you just have to choose which one it is nearest to.

Approximate answers

Estimating is a bit like guessing – but we use information for an approximate answer, rather than a wild guess!

Always work out an approximate answer before you calculate, then you will know if your actual answer makes sense. Use rounding skills to work out an approximate answer for the following example.

There are 38 magazines in a box. How many are there in 9 boxes?

> 38 rounds up to 40.
>
> $40 \times 9 = 360$
>
> 38×9 is approximately 360.

 Key words   rounding   estimating   approximate answer

Rounding

Round each of these numbers to the nearest 10.

1 64 → ☐

2 72 → ☐

3 38 → ☐

4 55 → ☐

5 911 → ☐

6 426 → ☐

7 803 → ☐

8 145 → ☐

8

Approximate answers

Circle the number that is nearest to the correct answer for each of these.

1 $47 + 32$ = 70 80 90

2 $19 + 27$ = 50 40 30

3 $82 + 71$ = 140 150 160

4 $91 - 18$ = 80 70 60

5 $66 - 41$ = 20 30 40

6 $102 - 39$ = 80 70 60

7 23×7 = 210 200 140

8 38×4 = 120 160 180

8

TOTAL MARKS 16

Fractions

Types of fractions

Look at these three types of fraction.

A **proper fraction**, such as $\frac{3}{5}$, which is less than 1.

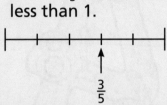

$\frac{3}{5}$

An **improper fraction**, such as $\frac{9}{4}$, which is greater than 1.

$\frac{9}{4} = 2\frac{1}{4}$

A **mixed number**, such as $2\frac{1}{4}$, which has whole numbers and fractions.

Parts of a fraction

A fraction has two parts:

$\dfrac{2}{3}$ ← numerator
← denominator

Top Tip
The bottom number shows the number of equal parts in total. The top number shows how many equal parts are taken.

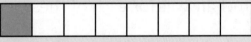

1 part out of 8 is shaded. This shows $\frac{1}{8}$.

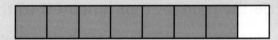

7 parts out of 8 are shaded. This shows $\frac{7}{8}$.

Equivalent fractions

Equivalent fractions are worth the same, even though they may look different. Imagine cutting a pizza into quarters and eating two of the pieces. Eating $\frac{2}{4}$ of a pizza is the same as eating $\frac{1}{2}$ of the pizza.

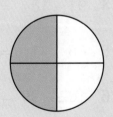

 Key words
proper fraction   improper fraction   mixed number
numerator   denominator   equivalent fractions

Types of fractions

Put a tick (✔) in each column to complete this table.
One has been done for you.

	$\frac{7}{3}$	$4\frac{2}{5}$	$\frac{10}{9}$	$\frac{4}{5}$	$\frac{3}{7}$	$3\frac{2}{3}$	$\frac{5}{2}$
Proper fraction							
Improper fraction	✔						
Mixed number							

6

Parts of a fraction

Write the fraction of each shape shaded blue.

1

4

2

5

3

6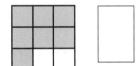

6

Equivalent fractions

Circle two fractions with the same value in each set.

1 $\frac{4}{6}$ $\frac{2}{10}$ $\frac{1}{2}$ $\frac{1}{4}$ $\frac{3}{6}$

2 $\frac{1}{4}$ $\frac{1}{2}$ $\frac{4}{10}$ $\frac{2}{8}$ $\frac{1}{5}$

3 $\frac{2}{6}$ $\frac{1}{4}$ $\frac{1}{2}$ $\frac{1}{3}$ $\frac{1}{5}$

4 $\frac{2}{5}$ $\frac{2}{20}$ $\frac{2}{10}$ $\frac{1}{12}$ $\frac{1}{10}$

5 $\frac{1}{3}$ $\frac{3}{9}$ $\frac{3}{10}$ $\frac{2}{3}$ $\frac{2}{9}$

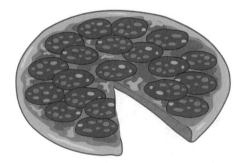

5

TOTAL MARKS 17

Addition and subtraction facts

Number facts

You need to know all of your number bonds to 20.
Number bonds are the addition and subtraction facts within 20.

Here are some examples.

$7 + 7$ $7 + 8$ $7 + 9$

$16 - 6$ $16 - 5$ $16 - 4$

You can use these facts to add and subtract tens.

$3 + 5 = 8$ $9 - 6 = 3$

3 tens + 5 tens = 8 tens   9 tens − 6 tens = 3 tens

$30 + 50 = 80$ $90 - 60 = 30$

Top Tip *If you start at 0 and count on in tens, you will find multiples of 10.*
10 20 30 40 50 60 70 80 90 100

Trios

The three numbers 8, 5 and 3 are called a trio.
They can make four addition and subtraction facts.

$3 + 5 = 8$ $5 + 3 = 8$ $8 - 5 = 3$ $8 - 3 = 5$

If you learn your addition facts, you can use them to help with subtraction.

$4 + 9 = 13$ $\boxed{} - 9 = 4$ $13 - \boxed{} = 9$

Top Tip *Remember that 4 + 6 gives the same answer as 6 + 4. It doesn't matter which way round you add. Once you know one fact, you know the other.*

Key words   multiple

Number facts

Answer these additions and subtractions.

1 2 + 9 = ☐

2 12 − 4 = ☐

3 8 + 7 = ☐

4 16 − 3 = ☐

5 11 + 6 = ☐

6 70 − 50 = ☐

7 30 + 40 = ☐

8 90 − 80 = ☐

9 60 + 20 = ☐

10 100 − 50 = ☐

☐ 10

Trios

Use these trios to find the missing numbers in each addition and subtraction.

| 4 | 5 | 9 |

1 4 + 5 = ☐

4 ☐ − 7 = 3

| 3 | 10 | 7 |

2 9 − ☐ = 5

5 14 − 8 = ☐

| 8 | 6 | 14 |

3 7 + 3 = ☐

6 8 + ☐ = 14

☐ 6

TOTAL MARKS ☐ 16

Multiplication facts

Times tables

Learning your tables will make the rest of the maths easier. Once you know these, you will never forget them.

On the grid, try to find $6 \times 4 = 24$.

You will see it is written twice, showing that the answer is the same for both: $6 \times 4 = 4 \times 6$.

×	1	2	3	4	5	6	7	8	9	10
1	1	2	3	4	5	6	7	8	9	10
2	2	4	6	8	10	12	14	16	18	20
3	3	6	9	12	15	18	21	24	27	30
4	4	8	12	16	20	24	28	32	36	40
5	5	10	15	20	25	30	35	40	45	50
6	6	12	18	24	30	36	42	48	54	60
10	10	20	30	40	50	60	70	80	90	100

Write down any facts you are not sure of and try to learn them. Use other facts to help.

> 8×3 is **double** 4×3.
>
> 9×3 is 3 less than 10×3, which is 27.
>
> 7×4 is double 7×2. Double 14 is 28.

Once you learn these, you can try your 7, 8 and 9 times tables.

 These are the facts for the tables that probably cause the most problems:

6 x 3	7 x 3	8 x 3	9 x 3
6 x 4	7 x 4	8 x 4	9 x 4

Learn one fact a day – it will only take 8 days!

Multiples

It is useful to be able to recognise multiples of 2, 5 and 10.

Multiples of 2 end in 0, 2, 4, 6, 8.

18 is a multiple of 2.

Multiples of 5 end in 0 or 5.

35 is a multiple of 5.

Multiples of 10 end in 0.

60 is a multiple of 2, 5 and 10.

Key words   double   even number

Times tables

Answer these questions.

1 $7 \times 2 =$ ☐

2 $5 \times 4 =$ ☐

3 $3 \times 6 =$ ☐

4 $4 \times 4 =$ ☐

5 $9 \times 5 =$ ☐

6 What is three multiplied by nine? ☐

7 Multiply seven by four. ☐

8 Double eight. ☐

9 There are six cakes in a packet. How many cakes are there in five packets? ☐

10 There are seven days in a week. How many days are there in ten weeks? ☐

💡 **Top Tip** *Remember that even numbers are all multiples of 2.*

10

Multiples

Use this list of multiples to answer each question.

> 50   15   8   14   9   20

1 Which numbers are multiples of 10? _____

2 Which numbers are multiples of 2? _____

3 Which numbers are multiples of 5? _____

4 Which number is a multiple of 5, but not a multiple of 2 or 10? _____

5 Which two numbers are multiples of 2, but not multiples of 10 or 5? _____

6 Which two numbers are multiples of 3? _____

6

TOTAL MARKS ☐ 16

Division facts

Dividing

Dividing is the opposite of multiplying. It is the same as sharing or grouping.

These both show 15 divided by 3.

15 sweets shared between 3.
There are 5 in each group.

$15 \div 3 = 5$

15 sweets grouped into 3s.
There are 5 groups.

$15 \div 3 = 5$

Top Tip

Remember that multiplication and division are inverses (opposites). Because of this, division can be checked by multiplying.
$35 \div 5 = $ ➜ $5 \times 7 = 35$ ➜ so $35 \div 5 = 7$

Missing number problems

15, 5 and 3 are a special set of numbers. We call them a trio, as you will have read on page 20.

$3 \times 5 = 15$ $5 \times 3 = 15$ $15 \div 3 = 5$ $15 \div 5 = 3$

Knowing your trios can help work out missing number problems.
2, 6 and 12 are another trio. Use them to find the missing numbers.

$2 \times \underline{\quad} = 12$ $\underline{\quad} \times 2 = 12$ $12 \div \underline{\quad} = 6$ $\underline{\quad} \div 6 = 2$

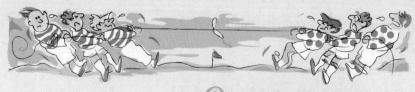

Key words   inverse

Dividing

1 Divide twelve by three. ☐

2 How many fives are there in forty? ☐

3 What is twenty-eight shared equally between four? ☐

4 What is half of eighteen? ☐

5 A class of 32 children are put into 4 equal teams. How many children are in each team? ☐

6 How many 5p stamps can be bought with 30p? ☐

7 27 counters are divided equally between 3 pots. How many counters will there be in each pot? ☐

8 There are 28g of yoghurt in a pot. Half the yoghurt has been eaten. How much yoghurt is left? ☐ g

8

Missing number problems

Write the missing numbers.

1 $70 \div \boxed{} = 10$

2 $\boxed{} \times 2 = 16$

3 $4 \times \boxed{} = 20$

4 $45 \div \boxed{} = 5$

5 $\boxed{} \times 3 = 18$

6 $\boxed{} \div 2 = 7$

7 $5 \times \boxed{} = 25$

8 $24 \div \boxed{} = 4$

1.) 5×5=25
2.) 25÷5=5
3.) 10÷2=5
4.) 3×5=15
5.) 45÷9=5

8

TOTAL MARKS ☐ 16

Mental addition and subtraction

Adding 2-digit numbers

If you need to add two big numbers, it helps to
break the numbers up and add the tens,
then add the ones.

15 + 37 = _____

Use these three steps.

1   Hold the bigger number in your head: 37.

2   Break 15 into 10 + 5. Then add the tens: 37 + 10 = 47.

3   Finally, add the ones: 47 + 5 = 52.

Counting on

A really good method for a take-away or subtraction is to find the
difference between the numbers by counting on.

What is the difference between 18 and 34?

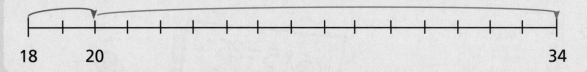

18   20   34

This number line shows exactly what goes on in your head.

Count on from 18 to 20. Hold the 2 in your head.

20 to 34 is 14.   14 + 2 is 16.   So 34 − 18 = 16.

 Top Tip   *If it helps, draw a quick number
line and show the steps. Remember
to put the smallest number on the
left and the largest on the right.*

Adding 2-digit numbers

Calculate these additions and write the matching letters
to find the code words. Each letter is worth one mark.

1 14 + 23 = ☐ → ☐

64 + 11 = ☐ → ☐

34 + 24 = ☐ → ☐

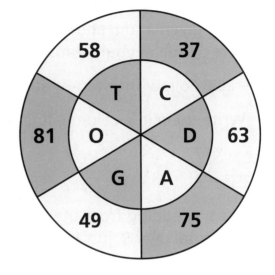

2 28 + 35 = ☐ → ☐

59 + 22 = ☐ → ☐

33 + 16 = ☐ → ☐

3 24 + 25 = ☐ → ☐

37 + 44 = ☐ → ☐

48 + 27 = ☐ → ☐

19 + 39 = ☐ → ☐

4 23 + 35 = ☐ → ☐

45 + 36 = ☐ → ☐

56 + 19 = ☐ → ☐

17 + 46 = ☐ → ☐

14

Counting on

Read and answer these questions.

1 What is the difference between 29 and 52? ☐

2 How much less is 38 than 83? ☐

3 Calculate the difference between 47 and 15. ☐

4 How much more is 64 than 43? ☐

5 Find the difference between 16 and 39. ☐

6 What is the difference between 21 and 78? ☐

6

TOTAL MARKS ☐ 20

Written addition

Written method for adding

If you are given a sum and the numbers are too big or there are too many numbers to add in your head, then you need to use a written method.

417 + 265 Follow this step-by-step method.

1   Write them in a column, lining up the units digits.

```
  417
+ 265
```

2   Start by adding from the right-hand column, the units column. Any total over 9, just put the tens digit under the next column.

```
  417
+ 265
    2
  1
```

3   Now do the same with the tens column. Keep going left until all the columns have been added.

```
  417
+ 265
  682
  1
```

Top Tip Work out an approximate answer first. 417 + 265 is approximately 400 + 300, which is 700. You can then check if your answer is close to your estimate.

Adding money

It can be a bit confusing if you need to add mixed amounts of pounds and pence. What is the total cost of a drink that is £1.60 and a cake at 79p?

Try changing the pence to pounds, lining up the decimal point.

```
  1.60
+ 0.79
  2.39
  1
```

79p

£1.60

The total cost is £2.39.

Key words   column   estimate

Written method for adding

Calculate these additions.

1   408
      + 257
      ———

2   361
      + 429
      ———

3   515
      + 185
      ———

4   146
      + 277
      ———

5 Add together 362 and 539.

6 What is the total of 444 and 198?

7 Calculate 207 + 595.

8 Add 487 and 416.

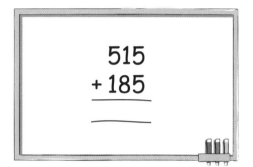

515
+185
———

8

Adding money

Calculate the total cost.

£3.40   £1.09   £1.59   75p   88p

1  £ ☐

2  £ ☐

3 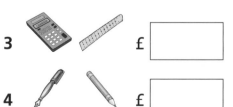 £ ☐

4 £ ☐

5  £ ☐

6  £ ☐

7  £ ☐

8  £ ☐

8

TOTAL MARKS ☐ 16

Written subtraction

Column method

If you cannot work out a subtraction in your head, this is one method you can try.

What is 874 subtract 138?

Step 1

Rename 70 + 4 as 60 + 14.

14 − 8 = 6

$$8\,{}^6 7\,{}^1 4$$
$$-\ 1\ 3\ 8$$
$$\overline{6}$$

Step 2

60 − 30 = 30

$$8\,{}^6 7\,{}^1 4$$
$$-\ 1\ 3\ 8$$
$$\overline{3\ 6}$$

Step 3

800 − 100 = 700

$$8\,{}^6 7\,{}^1 4$$
$$-\ 1\ 3\ 8$$
$$\overline{7\ 3\ 6}$$

Top Tip

Important! Remember to always take the bottom number away from the top number.

Number line method

Another written method is to use a number line to find the difference between the numbers by counting on.

What is 173 subtract 138?

1. Draw a blank number line from 138 to 173.

2. Count on to 140, then to 173 to find the difference.

```
        +2              +33
   138   140                        173
```

3. Add up all the jumps.

2 + 33 = 35, so the difference between 138 and 173 is 35.

Column method

Complete these subtractions.

1
```
   4 9 3
 - 1 5 5
 _____
```

2
```
   7 0 2
 - 6 8 2
 _____
```

3
```
   5 3 7
 - 1 4 9
 _____
```

4
```
   8 2 6
 -  2 1 8
 _____
```

5 Subtract 165 from 368.

6 What number is 294 less than 750?

7 Calculate 411 – 172.

8 What is 603 minus 359?

9 What is 527 subtract 188?

9

Number line method

Use the number lines to answer these.

1 What is the difference between 436 and 481?

436   481

2 What is the difference between 597 and 617?

597   617

3 What is the difference between 215 and 400?

215   400

4 What is the difference between 350 and 523?

350   523

4

TOTAL MARKS   13

Multiplication

Mental calculations

If you know your tables, then multiplying numbers to 20 by a single digit can be worked out in your head.

What is 13 multiplied by 4?

Use these three steps.

> 1 Multiply the tens: $10 \times 4 = 40$.
>
> 2 Multiply the units: $3 \times 4 = 12$.
>
> 3 Add the two parts: $40 + 12 = 52$.

 Top Tip *To multiply tens by a single digit, work out the fact and then make it ten times bigger:*

$60 \times 4 = 6 \times 4 \times 10 = 24 \times 10 = 240$

Written methods

To work out a multiplication such as 38×5, you need to be able to multiply multiples of 10.

$38 = 30 + 8$

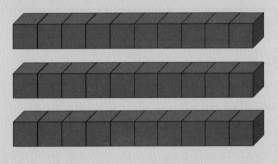

$+$

38×5	$\rightarrow$	30×5	150
		8×5	40 +
		38×5	190

Look at these two methods for this.

```
    3 8
  ×   5
  -----
    190
      4
```

×	30	8
5	150	40

$\boxed{150} + \boxed{40} = 190$

Mental calculations

Write the missing numbers to complete this multiplication grid.

×	14	19	17
5			
3			

  6

Written methods

Answer these.

1 28 × 4 =

$$\begin{array}{r} 28 \\ \times\ 4 \\ \hline \end{array}$$

2 54 × 6 =

$$\begin{array}{r} 54 \\ \times\ 6 \\ \hline \end{array}$$

3 49 × 3 =

×   40   9

3   [|]

[   ] + [   ] = [   ]

4 73 × 5 =

×   70   3

5   [|]

[   ] + [   ] = [   ]

5 What is thirty-seven multiplied by two? [   ]

6 Calculate 95 × 3. [   ]

7 A shop has 86 pairs of shoes. How many shoes are there altogether? [   ]

8 Golf balls are sold in packs of five. How many balls will there be in 44 packs? [   ]

9 A baker has baked enough rolls to fill 63 bags with 4 rolls each. How many bread rolls did he bake in total? [   ]

10 A school uses three 57-seater buses for a trip to a museum. All the seats are filled. How many tickets will be needed for the museum? [   ]

10

TOTAL MARKS [   ] 16

Division

Doubling and halving

An important thing to remember about division is that it is the inverse or opposite of multiplication.

$$40 \div 2 = \underline{\quad} \qquad 20 \times 2 = 40$$

It is very useful to be able to double and halve numbers. Look at this doubling machine.

$$14 \rightarrow \boxed{\text{IN} \quad \text{DOUBLE} \quad \text{OUT}} \rightarrow 28$$

When a number goes in, it is doubled. If 32 goes in, 64 comes out.

What if you put numbers backwards through the machine? Can you see that it becomes a halving machine?

For example, half of 28 is 14 and half of 64 is 32.

Top Tip *Doubling is the same as multiplying by 2 and halving is the same as dividing by 2.*

Halving is the opposite of doubling.

Division and remainders

Many division answers are not exact. They have an amount left over. For example, if you wanted to put 35 pencils into boxes, with 4 pencils in each box, there would be some pencils left over. If a number cannot be divided exactly, it leaves a remainder.

Work out how many groups of 4 are in 35 and what is left over:

```
      8 r 3
   4 | 3 5
   -   3 2   (4 × 8)      35 ÷ 4 = 8 remainder 3
   _____
       3
```

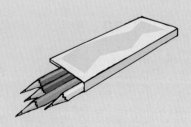

Key words   halve   remainder

Doubling and halving

Write the missing numbers for each function machine.

1 9
2 16
3 37
4 45

5 86
6 26
7 58
8 48

8

Division and remainders

Answer these questions. Use the box to show your method for the first four.

1 $3\overline{)68}$ = ☐

2 $79 \div 4$ = ☐

3 $4\overline{)91}$ = ☐

4 $52 \div 3$ = ☐

5 Circle the number that has a remainder of 2 when divided by 5.

33   68   47   54

6 What is the remainder when you divide fifty-two by six? ☐

7 Twenty-five eggs are put into boxes holding six eggs each.
   There is one egg left over.
   How many egg boxes are used? ☐

7

TOTAL MARKS 15

Fractions of quantities

Fractions of shapes

When you are asked to work out fractions of shapes, you may need to work out equivalent fractions. Remember to find the number of equal parts (the denominator or bottom number of the fraction) and then how many parts are shaded (the numerator or top number of the fraction).

What fraction of the rectangle is shaded?

> The rectangle is divided into 8 equal parts and 2 parts are shaded.
>
> $$\frac{2}{8} \quad \frac{\div 2}{\div 2} = \frac{1}{4}$$

Fractions and division

Look at these examples.

> What is:
>
> $\frac{1}{3}$ of 15?　　　　$\frac{1}{5}$ of 20?　　　　$\frac{1}{4}$ of 12?
>
> 　　

These all have 1 as a numerator, so simply divide by the denominator.

$\frac{1}{3}$ of 15	$\frac{1}{5}$ of 20	$\frac{1}{4}$ of 12
is	is	is
$15 \div 3 = 5$	$20 \div 5 = 4$	$12 \div 4 = 3$

Fractions of shapes

What fraction of each shape is shaded red?

1

4

2

5

3

6

6

Fractions and division

Use the balloons to answer these questions.

1   What is $\frac{1}{3}$ of 12?

2   What is $\frac{1}{4}$ of 16?

3   What is $\frac{1}{2}$ of 14?

4   What is $\frac{1}{5}$ of 10?

There are 24 balloons of different shapes and colours in a pack.
How many of each type of balloon are there?

5 $\frac{1}{4}$ are red   red balloons

6 $\frac{1}{2}$ are yellow   yellow balloons

7 $\frac{1}{6}$ are blue   blue balloons

8 $\frac{1}{3}$ are large balloons   large balloons

9 $\frac{1}{8}$ are long balloons   long balloons

9

TOTAL MARKS   15   37

Symmetry

Lines of symmetry

Some shapes are **symmetrical** – they have lines of symmetry. Look at the shape.

If you imagine it folded down the middle, the two sides would look exactly the same. That fold line is the line of symmetry and shows if a shape or pattern is symmetrical.

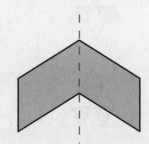

These letters are symmetrical.
Can you see the lines of symmetry?

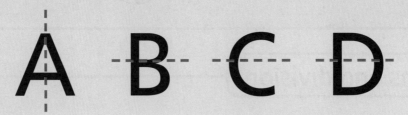

Reflections

You may be asked to draw the reflection of a picture or pattern so that it is symmetrical. The mirror line is always drawn to help and the shapes are usually drawn on a grid. Use the squares on the grid to help you work out the position of each corner of the shape.

Draw the reflection of this shape.

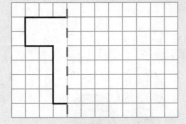

Imagine the line is a mirror. Draw dots on each corner and count the squares across, so that each point is reflected.

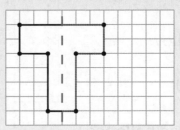

Top Tip: When a mirror is put on the line of symmetry, the half shape and its reflection show the whole shape. Practise using a small mirror to help you find symmetrical shapes.

Key words | symmetrical

Lines of symmetry

Draw one line of symmetry on each of these shapes.

1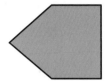

2

3

4

5

6

7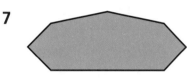

8

8

Reflections

Complete these reflections.

1 Use a ruler to draw lines to make a symmetrical shape about the mirror line.

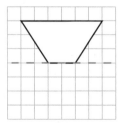

2 Shade in the reflection of this shape. You may use a mirror.

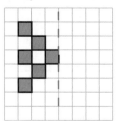

3 Here is a square with a design on it. The square is reflected in the mirror line. Draw the missing stripe and circle on the reflected square.

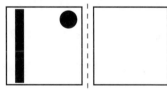

4 Draw the reflection of this triangle.

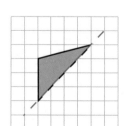

4

TOTAL MARKS 12

2D shapes

Polygons

Any shape with straight sides is called a **polygon**.
The name of the polygon tells you the number of sides.

3 sides	Triangle	
4 sides	Quadrilateral	
5 sides	Pentagon	
6 sides	Hexagon	
7 sides	Heptagon	
8 sides	Octagon	

Regular polygons

Regular polygons are shapes with all sides of equal length and all angles the same size.

Some regular shapes have special names.

A regular triangle is an **equilateral triangle**.

A regular quadrilateral is a **square**.

 When you look at shapes, check their sides and angles. Remember that parallel sides never meet and right angles are like square angles.

Another special four-sided shape is a **rectangle**. It has four **right angles** and two pairs of **parallel** sides, which are the same length.

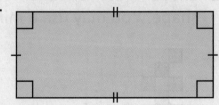

 Key words   **polygon   right angle   parallel**

Polygons

Count the number of sides and write the name of each shape.

1

☐ _____

2

☐ _____

3

☐ _____

4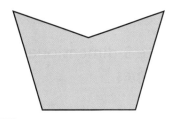

☐ _____

5

☐ _____

6

☐ _____

6

Regular polygons

Complete this table. Write in the missing cross (✗) or tick (✔) in each space.

Shape	Property of shape		
	4 sides	A regular shape	1 or more right angles
▭		✗	
⬡	✗		
⬠			✔
◻	✔		
▲			✗

10

TOTAL MARKS ☐ 16

3D solids

Names of 3D shapes

Solid shapes are 3-dimensional. You need to learn the names and properties of these 3D shapes.

cube   cuboid   cylinder   tetrahedron

cone   triangular prism   sphere   square-based pyramid

 A cube is a special cuboid and a cuboid is a type of prism. Can you see how a cuboid has some properties similar to a triangular prism?

Parts of solid shapes

Solid shapes are made up of **faces**, **edges** and **vertices** or corners.

A face is a surface of a solid.

An edge is where two faces meet.

A vertex is where three or more edges meet.

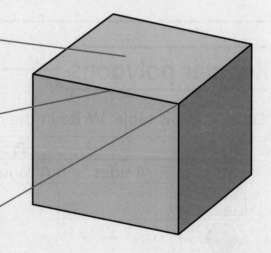

 Some shapes have flat faces and some are curved. A cylinder has 2 flat faces and 1 curved face.

 Key words   **face   edge   vertex/vertices**

Names of 3D shapes

Write the shape name of each of these everyday objects.

1

_____

2

_____

3

_____

4

_____

5

_____

6

_____

7

_____

8

_____

8

Parts of solid shapes

Read and answer these questions.

1 How many faces are triangles on a square-based pyramid? _____

2 Which solid shape has 6 square faces and 12 edges? _____

3 I am thinking of a 3D shape. It has 4 triangle
faces and 4 vertices. What shape am I thinking of? _____

4 Which 3D shape has one curved face and no edges? _____

4

TOTAL MARKS 12

Angles

Right angles

Corners of doors, windows, books and tables all show right angles.

These are **square angles** and can be seen all around us.

A right angle is a quarter turn, **clockwise** or **anticlockwise**.

Squares and rectangles have four right angles – one at each corner.

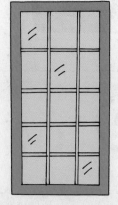

Types of angles

An angle is a measure of turn between two lines. Angles are measured in degrees (°).

There are 360° in a full circle.

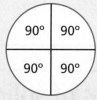

| 90° | 90° |
| 90° | 90° |

These are special angles to remember.

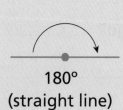

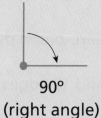

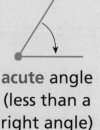

| 180° (straight line) | 90° (right angle) | **acute** angle (less than a right angle) | **obtuse** angle (between 90° and 180°) |

Use a right-angle corner from a piece of paper to compare angles, to see if they are acute or obtuse.

Key words   clockwise   anticlockwise   acute   obtuse

Right angles

Circle all of the right angles on each shape.

1 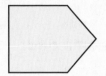   **2**   **3**   **4**

Read the instructions and circle the arrow pointing in the correct direction.

5 This arrow is rotated 90° clockwise.

6 This arrow is rotated 90° anticlockwise.

7 This arrow is rotated 90° anticlockwise.

8 This arrow is rotated 90° clockwise.

8

Types of angles

Look at these angles and answer the questions.

a   **b**    **c**   **d**   **e**

1 Which is the smallest angle? ☐

2 Which angle is a straight line? ☐

3 Which is a right angle? ☐

4 Which angle is obtuse? ☐

5 Which angle is 90°? ☐

6 Which two angles are acute?

☐ and ☐

7 Which angle is 180°? ☐

8 Which is the largest angle? ☐

8

TOTAL MARKS ☐ 16

Position and direction

Coordinates

Coordinates are used to show the exact position of a point on a grid.

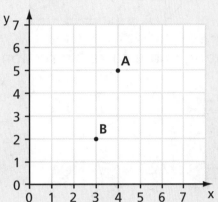

The coordinates of **A** are (4,5).

The coordinates of **B** are (3,2).

Coordinates are always written in brackets and separated by a comma.

Remember to read the horizontal number along the bottom and then the vertical number up the side.

Points of the compass

It is useful to know the points of the compass. North and South are opposite each other, as are East and West. In between these are the other four points. Look at the way their names always start with North or South.

Top Tip

To remember the order of the four main directions, look at the initials NESW. A well-known saying to learn this order is Naughty Elephants Squirt Water!

Directions

Clockwise and anticlockwise are instructions for moving in different directions. Quarter turns, half turns and whole turns are used to describe how far to turn.

This arrow has moved a quarter turn clockwise.

This arrow has moved a half turn anticlockwise.

A whole turn is a complete circle. This is a whole turn clockwise.

🔑 Key words   **horizontal   vertical**

Coordinates

1 Circle the correct coordinates for point **A**.

(1,1)   (1,2)   (2,1)   (2,2)

2 Write the coordinates for point **B**.

(☐ , ☐)

3 Write the coordinates for point **C**.

(☐ , ☐)

4 Draw a cross at (5,10) and label it **D**.

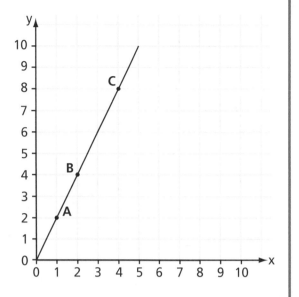

4

Points of the compass

The arrow labelled N is pointing North.

1 Label the arrows pointing South, West and East.

2 Colour the arrow pointing North-West.

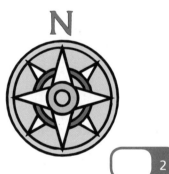

2

Directions

Look at the compass points to help you answer these.

1 If I face North and make a half turn clockwise, which direction will I be facing? _____

2 If I face South and make a quarter turn clockwise, which direction will I be facing? _____

3 If I face North-West and make a half turn anticlockwise, which direction will I be facing? _____

3

TOTAL MARKS ☐ 9

Measures

Units of measure

Length, weight (or mass) and capacity are all measured using different units. Try to learn these:

Length	1 centimetre (cm) = 10 millimetres (mm) 1 metre (m) = 100 centimetres (cm) 1 kilometre (km) = 1000 metres (m)
Weight	1 kilogram (kg) = 1000 grams (g)
Capacity	1 litre (l) = 1000 millilitres (ml)

Top Tip

Remember to always write the units in your answers. There is a big difference between 100g and 100kg!

Converting units

Once you know these equivalent measures, then you can convert from one unit to another. This always means multiplying or dividing by 10, 100 or 1000, depending on what you are converting.

My finger is 6.3cm or 63mm long.

A lemonade bottle holds 3000ml or 3 litres.

This cake weighs 1.3kg or 1300g.

20 times around a 400m running track is 8000m or 8km.

Reading scales

A scale is the marking of lines to help us measure, e.g. up the side of a jug, on weighing scales or on a ruler. You need to read them carefully, using these steps:

1　Look at the unit – is it ml, cm, mm, g … ?

2　If the line is level with a number, read off that number.

3　If the line is between numbers, work out what each mark means and count on or back.

Key words　　equivalent

Units of measure

Underline the amount each item is most likely to measure.

1 My pencil is (14mm) (14cm) (14m) (14km) long.

2 I bought a (2ml) (20ml) (2 litre) (20 litre) carton of milk.

3 The classroom door is (2mm) (2cm) (2m) (2km) high.

4 An apple weighs (6g) (60g) (6kg) (60kg).

5 I travel (3mm) (3cm) (3m) (3km) to school every day.

5

Converting units

Answer these questions.

1 How many millilitres are there in four litres? [ ] ml

2 How many metres are there in five and a half kilometres? [ ] m

3 How many centimetres are there in seven metres? [ ] cm

4 How many grams are there in three and a half kilograms? [ ] g

5 How many millimetres are there in twelve centimetres? [ ] mm

5

Reading scales

Measure these sides with a ruler.

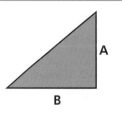

1 Use a ruler to measure the length of side **A**.
Give your answer in centimetres. [ ] cm

2 Measure accurately the length of side **B**.
Give your answer in millimetres. [ ] mm

2

TOTAL MARKS [ ] 12

Perimeter and area

Finding perimeters

The **perimeter** of a shape is simply the distance all the way around the edge. These two shapes have the same perimeter of 16cm.

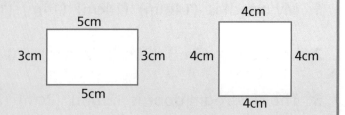

If the shape has straight sides, add up the lengths of all the sides. These may be given, or you may need to measure carefully along each of the sides using a ruler.

3cm + 3cm + 4cm + 4cm + 6cm = 20cm

The perimeter of this shape is 20cm.

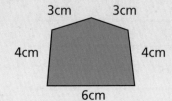

If the shape has curved sides, a piece of string or cotton may be useful. Go around the edge of the shape and then measure the length of the piece of thread.

This shape has a perimeter of 10cm.

Finding areas

The **area** of a shape is the amount of surface that it covers. You can often measure the area of shapes by counting squares.

These shapes both have an area of 8 squares.

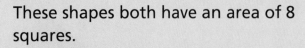

If the shape is not made up from whole squares, count all the squares that are bigger than a half.

This shape has an area of approximately 12 squares.

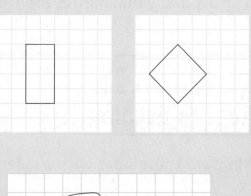

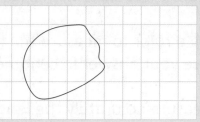

Key words   perimeter   area

Finding perimeters

Answer these questions.

1 This playground measures 35m by 27m.
What is the perimeter of this playground?

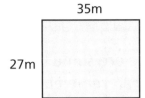
35m

27m

 m

2 A square carpet has a perimeter of 20m.
How long is one of its sides?

 m

3 Measure the sides of this rectangle.
What is the perimeter of this rectangle?

 cm

4 Calculate the perimeter of this triangle.

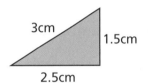
3cm   1.5cm
2.5cm

 cm

4

Finding areas

Count the squares and write the areas for each shape.

 1cm
1cm

1

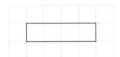

_____ square cm

3

_____ square cm

2

_____ square cm

4

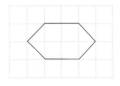

_____ square cm

4

TOTAL MARKS [ ] 8

Reading the time

Time facts

These are some time facts to learn. Cover each one up and see how many you can remember.

1 minute	= 60 seconds	1 week	= 7 days	
1 hour	= 60 minutes	1 fortnight	= 14 days	
1 day	= 24 hours	1 year	= 12 months = 365 days	
		leap year	= 366 days	

Use the 'knuckle method' to learn the days of the months:

31 days: January, March, May, July, August, October, December.

All the 'knuckle months' have 31 days. February has 28 days (29 days in a leap year) and April, June, September and November have 30 days.

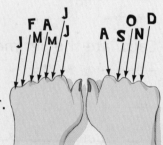

Or you can remember:
30 days has September, April, June and November.
All the rest have 31, except February which has 28 days clear and 29 each leap year.

Telling the time

Reading a circular clock face.

If you find it difficult to tell the time, then follow these three easy steps.

1   Look at the short hour hand on your clock or watch and say the last hour that this has gone past. This has gone past the 5, so it is past 5 o'clock.

2   Look at the longer minute hand and count around in fives from the top to the hand: 5, 10, 15, 20, 25, 30, 35, 40.

3   Say aloud the hour followed by the number of minutes – so you say 5.40, which means 40 minutes past 5.

Key words   leap year

Time facts

Answer these questions.

1 How many days are there in four weeks?   _____

2 A film is an hour and a half long.
   How many minutes is this?   _____

3 If today is Monday 10th August, what day
   of the week will 17th August be?   _____

4 How many months are there in three years?   _____

5 How many more days are there in a leap year
   than a normal year?   _____

6 If today is 1st May, what was the date yesterday? _____

6

Telling the time

Draw the missing hands to show these times. Remember to draw the hour
hand shorter than the minute hand.

1

quarter past ten

2

6.10

3

twenty past eight

4

11.25

5

quarter to one

6

9.55

6

TOTAL MARKS   12

Handling data

Bar charts

Bar charts are a useful way of showing information. To understand bar charts and other types of graph, look carefully at the different parts of the graph.

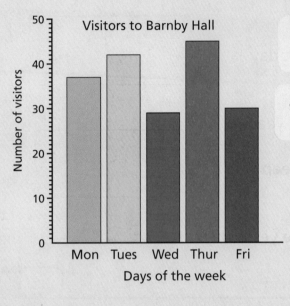

1 Read the title – what is it all about? Is there any other information given?

2 Look at the **axis** labels – these should explain the lines that go up and across.

3 Work out the scale – look carefully at the numbers. Do they go up in 1s, 2s, 5s, 10s … ?

4 Compare the bars – read them across to work out the amounts.

 Top Tip *The scale is very important. This graph goes up in tens and some of the bars are between tens. For example, there were between 40 and 50 visitors on Tuesday. To read this, go across from the top of the bar and count on from 40 to 42.*

Pictograms

Pictograms use symbols or pictures, where each symbol represents a certain number of items.

This is a record of the numbers of frogs seen crossing a road in a morning.

 = 2 frogs

Time	Number of frogs
7:00 – 8:00	🐸🐸🐸🐸
8:00 – 9:00	🐸🐸🐸🐸🐸🐸
9:00 – 10:00	🐸🐸🐸🐸🐸🐸🐸🐸
10:00 – 11:00	🐸🐸🐸🐸🐸
11:00 – 12:00	🐸🐸🐸

 Top Tip *Check what each individual picture stands for. This shows that 12 frogs were seen between 8.00 and 9.00am.*

 Key words axis

Bar charts

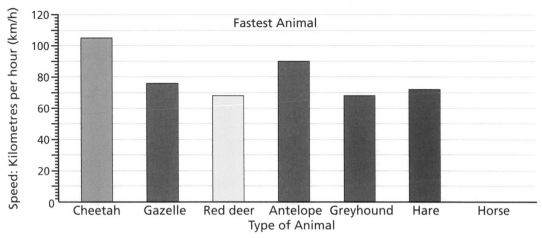

1 What speed can an antelope run? _____ km/h

2 Which is fastest, a greyhound or a hare? _____

3 The fastest speed recorded for a horse is 70km/h. Draw a bar to show this on the chart.

4 Which animal runs 20km/h faster than the horse? _____

4

Pictograms

 = 2 eggs   (= 1 egg

This pictogram shows the number of eggs collected from a group of chickens each day.

Days of the week	Number of eggs
Monday	◯ ◯
Tuesday	◯ ◯ ◯ (
Wednesday	◯ ◯ ◯
Thursday	◯ (
Friday	◯ ◯
Saturday	◯ ◯ (
Sunday	◯

1 On which day were the most eggs collected?

   _____

2 How many eggs were collected on Friday? _____

3 On which day were three eggs collected? _____

4 How many eggs were collected in total on Monday and Tuesday? _____

5 How many more eggs were collected on Saturday than Sunday? _____

5

Sorting diagrams

Venn diagrams

To sort these shapes into groups, you could use a Venn diagram.
This Venn diagram sorts the shapes by colour and shape.

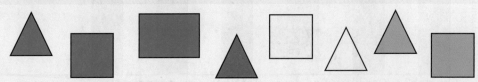

This shows the set of triangles.

This shows the set of blue shapes.

This shows shapes that are not blue or triangles.

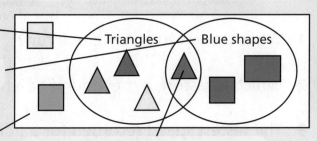

Triangles   Blue shapes

This shows blue shapes that are triangles.

Carroll diagrams

Carroll diagrams are very similar to Venn diagrams, but they use a grid rather than circles.

You can use a Carroll diagram to sort shapes, objects or numbers.

16   34   13   27   43   39   22   19   40   45

This shows even numbers that are greater than 20.

	even numbers	not even numbers
greater than 20	22, 34, 40	27, 39, 43, 45
not greater than 20	16	13, 19

This shows numbers that are not even and are greater than 20.

This shows the set of even numbers not greater than 20.

This shows the set of numbers not greater than 20 and not even.

 Key words   Venn diagram   Carroll diagram

Venn diagrams

Write the letter for each creature in the correct section of this Venn diagram. Then you could have a go at drawing them too!

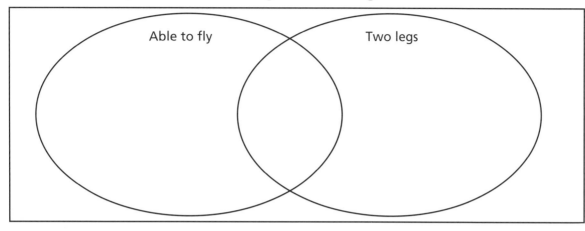

Able to fly   Two legs

a bee	e penguin 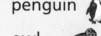
b human	f owl 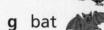
c seagull	g bat 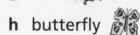
d spider	h butterfly

8

Carroll diagrams

Use these shapes to complete this Carroll diagram. You can either write the shape's letter or draw in the shape.

a   b   c   d   e   f  g   h

	1 or more right angles	No right angles
Quadrilateral		
Not a quadrilateral		

8

Glossary

acute an angle smaller than a right angle

anticlockwise turning in this direction

approximate answer a 'rough' answer – near to the real answer

area the area of a shape is the amount of surface that it covers

axis (plural is axes) the horizontal and vertical lines on a graph

Carroll diagram a grid used to sort things into groups or sets

clockwise turning in this direction

column a vertical arrangement of numbers, words or objects going up or down

consecutive one after the other in order. For example, 15, 16 and 17 are consecutive numbers

denominator the bottom number of a fraction, the number of parts it is divided into. Example: $\frac{2}{3}$

difference the difference between two numbers is the amount that one number is greater than the other. The difference between 18 and 21 is 3

digit there are 10 digits: 0 1 2 3 4 5 6 7 8 and 9 that make all the numbers we use

double make something twice as big, or multiply by 2

edge where two faces of a solid shape meet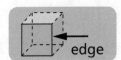

equivalent two numbers or measures are equivalent if they are the same or equal

equivalent fractions these are equal fractions. Example: $\frac{1}{2} = \frac{2}{4} = \frac{3}{6}$

estimate is like a good guess

even number a number that can be divided exactly by 2. Even numbers end in 0 2 4 6 or 8

face the flat side of a solid shape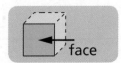

halve to cut an object or a group of objects into two equal parts, so there is $\frac{1}{2}$ in each

horizontal a horizontal line is a straight level line across, in the same direction as the horizon

improper fraction any fraction which is greater than 1, such as $\frac{5}{3}$, $\frac{8}{5}$ or $\frac{6}{2}$

inverse the opposite or reverse – addition is the inverse of subtraction

leap year every four years there are 366 days in a year. The extra day is the 29th February

mixed number any whole number and fraction written together, such as $2\frac{1}{2}$, $4\frac{3}{5}$ or $1\frac{3}{10}$

multiple a multiple is a number made by multiplying together two other numbers

numerator the top number of a fraction. Example: $\frac{3}{5}$

obtuse an angle less than 180° (a straight line) but greater than 90° (a right angle)

Glossary

parallel lines that are parallel never meet and the distance between the lines remains the same

perimeter the distance all the way around the edge of a shape or object

polygon any straight-sided flat shape

proper fraction any fraction which is less than 1, such as $\frac{2}{3}$, $\frac{3}{5}$ or $\frac{1}{10}$

remainder if a number cannot be divided exactly by another number, there is a whole number answer with an amount left over, called a remainder

right angle a quarter turn. The corner of a square is a right angle

rounding changing a number to the nearest ten. A 'round number' is a number ending in zero: 10, 20, 30, 40, 50, 60, 70, 80, 90 or 100

sequence a list of numbers which usually have a pattern. They are often numbers written in order

symmetrical when two halves of a shape or pattern are identical

total when you add some numbers, the answer is the total

Venn diagram a diagram that shows groups of things by putting circles around them

vertical a line that is straight up or down, at right angles to a horizontal line

vertices (single is vertex) the corners of 3D shapes, where edges meet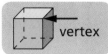

Speaking and listening skills

Taking turns

The **speaking and listening** skills you learn at school will help you to speak clearly to an audience and also to understand what other people are saying to you.

You might be asked to give your own presentation, or to listen to a presentation on a topic. Or you might be asked to discuss a topic with another person, or in a group. Very often, you will have to wait for your turn to speak.

When someone is speaking, it is polite to stay quiet. It also means you can listen carefully to what they say. You might even want to make some quick notes to remind you of the key points they make.

Getting ready to speak

Speaking in front of a group can be scary, but being properly prepared will make you more confident.

Start by gathering the information you need. You might need to do some research in books or on the Internet. If you are working in a team, discuss your ideas with the others in your team.

Make notes of your ideas and decide which are the most important. You should talk about these first.

Try to learn the main points you want to make, using your notes to help you.

Top Tip

Key words   speaking and listening

Taking turns

Working with a partner, discuss what you did over the summer holiday. Remember to take turns.

 Try jotting down single words while your partner is talking, to help you remember what they have said.

Write down two of the points you make about your holiday.

1 _____

_____

2 _____

_____

Write down two of the points your partner makes.

3 _____

_____

4 _____

_____

4

Getting ready to speak

Imagine you are planning a short presentation on one of your hobbies. Write down **four** key points you would like to make.

1 _____

2 _____

3 _____

4 _____

4

TOTAL MARKS 8

The language of books

On the cover

The first thing you see when you look at a book is the front cover. A lot of the features you find on the cover of a book are designed to encourage people to pick up the book and read it. Others are there to help bookshops and libraries.

blurb

ISBN

publisher

spine

title

cover illustration

author's name

written by **Stacey Brown**
illustrated by **John Davis**

illustrator's name

Inside books

The insides of books are designed to make reading them easier. Information books arrange their contents so that it is easy for readers to find what they need.

The contents list is at the front of the book. It lists the chapters or sections in the book, along with the page each starts on. Contents lists are arranged in page order.

The index is found at the back of the book. Indexes list subjects alphabetically, to help readers find information about a specific topic.

Information books often contain new words. Some books explain what these words mean. Often they are listed alphabetically at the back of the book, along with their definitions. This is called a glossary.

Top Tip

Look at the back of this book to see what a glossary looks like.

Key words   blurb   ISBN   index   glossary

On the cover

Think about your favourite book, or the book you are reading now. Design a new front cover for it. You will score one mark for including each of the following three things:
a title, a cover illustration and the name of the author.

 Top Tip *Try to make your cover illustration exciting, so that you hook readers.*

3

Inside books

Choose the correct option to complete each sentence. Underline your choice.

1   The contents list is found at the (back / front) of the book.

2   The index is arranged (alphabetically / in page order).

3   New words are explained in a (blurb / glossary).

4   There is a glossary at the (back / front) of this book.

5   The index is found at the (front / back) of the book.

5

TOTAL MARKS   8

Fiction and non-fiction

What is fiction?

Fiction is made-up writing. Most of the short stories and longer novels you read are fiction. They contain made-up characters and settings, and the events that happen are made up too.

Some fiction writing is based on a real person, or set in a real place. Other stories might be about real things that happened. However, most of the details come from the writer's imagination.

Fiction writing is designed to be read right the way through, so you can follow the story. Good fiction is so gripping that you don't want to put it down until you know what happens at the end!

What is non-fiction?

Non-fiction is information writing. Books about science, history or animals are all non-fiction and so are newspapers, adverts and instructions. This book is non-fiction too!

Non-fiction writing contains lots of facts. The information is usually organised into chapters or sections, so that readers can find what they need easily, rather than having to read the whole book.

You need to know the difference between fiction and non-fiction. It can be hard to tell sometimes, because writers often base fictional stories on real people or events.

Key words   fiction   non-fiction   fact

What is fiction?

Look at this pile of books. Can you tell by their titles which ones are fiction? Colour the fiction books red and the non-fiction books blue.

Top Tip *Non-fiction books often have straightforward titles that tell you exactly what is inside the book.*

5

What is non-fiction?

1 Do you enjoy non-fiction books? Or do you prefer fiction?

_____

_____

2 Write a sentence to explain why you think this is.

_____

_____

2

TOTAL MARKS   7

Reading skills

Skimming

Reading tests ask questions to check comprehension, or understanding, of a piece of writing. We read in different ways, depending on what we are trying to find out from a piece of writing.

When you see a piece of writing for the first time, you will often read through it quickly, to find out what it is about. You might also notice how it is organised. If it is fiction, perhaps you will notice where the characters first appear and what they are like. If it is non-fiction, you will be able to work out what kind of writing it is and spot where the topic changes.

Quick reading for meaning like this is called skimming.

Scanning

Once you have skimmed through the text and read the questions carefully, you are ready to look for the information you need to answer them.

Scanning means reading the text again, looking for a specific piece of information. It might be a person's name, a date or the name of a place. The way the question is worded will tell you what kind of information you need to look for.

Where did the family in the story move to?   Look for a place name.

When did Henry VIII come to the throne?   Look for a date.

Take care with scanning. There may be more than one place name or date in the text and you won't get any marks if you choose the wrong one!

Key words   comprehension   skimming   scanning

Skimming

Skim through this piece of text, then answer the questions.

For a week now, piles of clean, ironed laundry had been growing in the bedrooms of the Clarks' house. Milly's mum was working hard to get the family ready for their trip to Florida.

Like all ten-year-olds, Milly loved to try new things and swimming with the dolphins on this trip was all she thought about. That, and her dog Max, who would be going into kennels for the first time. She would miss him!

1 What is the piece of writing about? Circle your answer.

a family holiday   a kennel   laundry

2 Is the story about a girl or a boy?

_____

3 Do you think it is fiction or non-fiction?

_____

3

Scanning

Use your scanning skills to find the answers to these questions.

1 How old is Milly?   _____

2 What is her dog called?   _____

3 Where is the family going on holiday? _____

3

TOTAL MARKS 6

Authors and narrators

What is an author?

Someone who writes a piece of text is called an author.

Most fiction books only have one author, who writes the whole story. A fiction book is a story that comes from the imagination of the author.

Some non-fiction books have more than one author. This can happen where the book contains information about more than one topic and each author writes about the topic they know best. Other times, two authors will work together to research and write a non-fiction book about a single topic.

It is important to know the name of a book's author, because bookshops and libraries arrange books alphabetically, by author.

What is a narrator?

The narrator is the storyteller in a piece of fiction writing. Narrators tell the story from their point of view. Sometimes the narrator is the author. Remember that this type of narrator can see all of the characters all of the time and knows exactly how they are all feeling. Clever!

The boy ran across the park and headed towards the station.

Other times, the narrator is a character in the story. This type of narrator will tell the story through the eyes of the character.

I ran across the park and headed for the station.

 Non-fiction books don't have a narrator, because they don't tell a story. They are written in an impersonal way, to describe and explain the topic.

 Key words | author narrator character

What is an author?

Answer these questions about authors.

1 What is an author?

_____

_____

2 If a book has more than one author, is it more likely to be fiction or non-fiction?

_____

3 How do libraries and bookshops use the names of authors?

_____

_____

3

What is a narrator?

Answer these questions about narrators.

1 Write a sentence to explain what a narrator is.

_____

_____

2 In this piece of text, is the narrator a character in the story?

> Hearing steps in the hallway outside, I slipped behind the curtain, tucking my feet out of sight.

yes ☐   no ☐

 *If the narrator is a character in the story, you will see lots of words like **I**, **we**, **me**, **my** and **our**.*

2

TOTAL MARKS ⬭ 5

Life stories

Biography

A **biography** is the story of a person's life, written by someone else.

Quite often, biographies are about people from history. Writers do lots of research to find out about their lives.

> Her family moved to Somerset during the war. She and her brother started at the local school. At first the other children treated them with suspicion, but when the evacuees arrived from London it was easier to fit in.

Autobiography

Autobiographies are life stories too, but they are written by the person whose story they tell.

> My family moved to Somerset during the war. My brother and I started at the local school. At first the other children treated us with suspicion, but when the evacuees arrived from London it was easier to fit in.

 Top Tip *A curriculum vitae, or CV, is another type of life story. People write a CV when they are looking for a new job, to show their qualifications and experience.*

 Key words   biography   autobiography   curriculum vitae

Biography

Can you tell biography from autobiography? Decide whether each of these sentences is more likely to have come from a biography or an autobiography. Write B for biography, or A for autobiography, in the boxes.

1   He produced the first maps of New Zealand.

2   Our house had a small yard at the back, with an outside toilet.

3   Her dress designs are seen on catwalks across the globe.

4   I have always wanted to swim with dolphins.

5   My childhood dream came true when I made it into the Olympic team.

 Top Tip *The writers of autobiography are writing about their own lives, so they will use words like **I**, **me**, **my** and **our**.*

5

Autobiography

Imagine you are writing your autobiography. You will get one mark each for writing about where you were born, where you live now, your family, friends and school.

_____

_____

_____

_____

_____

_____

5

TOTAL MARKS 10

Sentences

Rules for sentences

A sentence is a group of words that work together to make sense on their own. They allow us to say what we think, ask questions and tell people what to do.

When we write sentences, there are some rules that we have to follow. The first word in a sentence must always start with a capital letter. This helps readers to understand that a new sentence has started.

Most sentences end with a full stop, but questions end with a question mark instead. If the sentence is delivering a surprise, or an order, it ends with an exclamation mark.

Is it time for dinner yet?

Look, it's snowing!

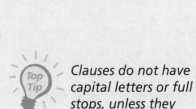

Clauses

A clause is part of a sentence that contains both a verb and a subject. A subject is the person or thing doing the action.

Some sentences just contain one clause. They are called simple sentences.

Ben ate the banana.

subject   verb

Some sentences contain more than one clause.

Ben ate the banana because he was hungry.

clause 1   clause 2

Often clauses in sentences are linked with joining words, like **because** in the example above.

> **Top Tip**
> Clauses do not have capital letters or full stops, unless they form a simple sentence.

 Key words | sentence   question mark   exclamation mark   clause
verb   subject   simple sentence

Rules for sentences

Can you find a mistake in each of these sentences? Circle them when you find them.

1 Stop that dreadful noise.

2 Where is my coat.

3 The bus was late, so we missed the start of the film

4 we are going to France on holiday.

5 it was my birthday on Friday.

5

Clauses

Decide which of these statements about clauses are true or false.

1 Simple sentences only contain one clause. _____

2 Sentences cannot contain more than one clause. _____

3 Clauses within sentences are often joined together with joining words. _____

4 Clauses do not contain a verb. _____

5 Clauses do not usually have a full stop or capital letter. _____

5

TOTAL MARKS 10

Contractions

How contractions work

Sometimes we use the same pairs of words so often that we can join them together. This is called contraction.

Words are contracted by removing one or more letters and replacing them with an apostrophe. Then you simply join the two words together.

I am = I'm   you will = you'll

I'm great at contractions and soon you'll be great too!

Top Tip *We use contraction all the time when we write conversation, or dialogue, for our characters. It is not usually used in more formal writing, like school work.*

Writing contracted forms

Here are some examples of contractions we use a lot.

she is	→	she's
does not	→	doesn't
he will	→	he'll
I have	→	I've
is not	→	isn't
who is	→	who's
you are	→	you're
they will	→	they'll
did not	→	didn't
they are	→	they're

I've got 10 sweets!

I haven't got any!

Key words   contraction   apostrophe   dialogue

How contractions work

Circle the correct contracted form for each pair of words.

1	he is	hei's	hes	he's
2	we will	well	we'll	we'l
3	she would	she'd	shew'd	she'ld
4	could not	couldnt	could't	couldn't
5	she will	she'll	she'l	shell

 Remember, the apostrophe goes in the place where the letters have been taken out.

5

Writing contracted forms

Can you write down the contracted forms of these word pairs?

1 you will _____

2 you have _____

3 we are _____

4 I would _____

5 should not _____

5

TOTAL MARKS 10

75

Possessive apostrophes

Using possessive apostrophes

Possessive apostrophes can be used to show that something belongs to someone or something.

You write them by adding an apostrophe followed by *s*.

the book that belongs to Sam = Sam's book

the basket that belongs to the dog = the dog's basket

the rattle that belongs to the baby = the baby's rattle

Possessive apostrophes for groups

Sometimes you will need to add a possessive apostrophe to a word that already ends in *s* because it is a plural.

In this case, you just add the apostrophe without adding another *s*.

the cars that belong to the teachers = the teachers' cars

the burrows that belong to the rabbits = the rabbits' burrows

the bags that belong to the boys = the boys' bags

 It is important to put the apostrophe in the correct place, because it is one of the ways your reader can tell whether you are talking about one person, or more than one.

 Key words　　　　　possessive apostrophe　plural

Using possessive apostrophes

Add the possessive apostrophe to each sentence.

1 Dawns shoes were too small.

2 I found the dogs lead and took him for a walk.

3 My sisters room is bigger than mine.

4 Tims birthday is next Friday.

5 A ducks feathers keep it warm and dry.

5

Possessive apostrophes for groups

Choose the correct word from the brackets to complete each sentence and write it in.

1 Three _____ faces appeared at the window. (boy's / boys')

2 All of our school _____ houses are a bus ride away. (friend's / friends')

3 All four _____ windows were decorated with Christmas lights. (shops' / shop's)

4 The sound of many _____ engines filled the air. (car's / cars')

5 Our two _____ claws had left scratches on the furniture. (cats' / cat's)

> **Top Tip** *When you are deciding where to put a possessive apostrophe, look at whether the sentence is talking about one person or thing, or more than one.*

5

TOTAL MARKS ___ 10

Punctuation

What is punctuation for?

We use **punctuation** to help our readers understand our writing. Punctuation marks work like a code to help readers to know when to pause, when someone is speaking and when a new topic is beginning. Without punctuation, reading would be much harder. Try reading this!

> marys feet slipped on the steep path and she lost her balance help she screamed her voice echoed around the canyon there was nobody to hear her she clung to the ledge and waited as the sun grew hotter

Ending sentences

Some of the most important punctuation marks end sentences. They tell readers that a sentence has finished and a new one is about to begin, and what kind of sentence it is.

Most sentences end with a full stop, but questions end with a question mark.

> I finished my book.   Have you seen Emily?

Sentences that deliver a surprise or an order end with an exclamation mark.

> Happy birthday!   Get out!

Commas

Commas are useful punctuation marks that help readers to make sense of sentences.

> Cackling loudly, the witch swept out of the cave.

Commas are also useful for separating the items in a list.

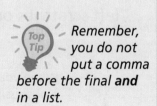

> We saw lions, tigers, giraffes and monkeys at the zoo.

*Remember, you do not put a comma before the final **and** in a list.*

 Key words   punctuation   comma

What is punctuation for?

Circle the punctuation marks in this piece of writing.

1 Greg ran down the stairs two at a time and bounded through the kitchen, grabbing a piece of toast on the way.

2 "Where are you off to?" asked Dad.

3 "I'm late for school!" panted Greg.

4 Dad laughed, "Greg, it's Saturday!"

 Top Tip *Speech marks go at the beginning and the end of what someone says. There is more about how to use them over the page.*

4

Ending sentences

Choose a full stop, question mark or exclamation mark to complete each sentence.

1 What time is it _____

2 We went to the theatre on Saturday _____

3 I don't believe it _____

4 How are you feeling _____

4

Commas

Add commas to these sentences.

1 I need to buy pencils a ruler and a sharpener for school.

2 Alex James Jack and Ali got parts in the school play.

3 I packed pyjamas slippers a toothbrush and toothpaste for the sleepover party.

4 We made a fruit smoothie with bananas strawberries raspberries and pears.

4

TOTAL MARKS   12

Writing about speech

Direct and reported speech

We often need to write about the things that people say.

Sometimes we write speech for our characters, so that they can talk to each other. We write the actual words that they say.

"What would you like for tea?" asked Dad.

This is called direct speech.

Other times we can write what someone says, without using their exact words.

Dad asked us what we wanted to eat.

This is called reported speech.

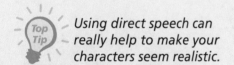

Top Tip: *Using direct speech can really help to make your characters seem realistic.*

Speech punctuation

When you write direct speech, you must use speech punctuation. It separates the speech from the rest of the sentence, so that your readers understand when someone is talking.

The teacher shouted, "Stop it!"

Speech marks go at the beginning and end of the speech, in pairs. When somebody is speaking, remember that their words always start with a capital letter, even if they are not at the start of a sentence.

 Key words   direct speech   reported speech   speech marks

Direct and reported speech

Decide whether each sentence contains direct or reported speech.
Write direct or reported at the end of each sentence.

1 "Have you seen my coat?" asked Sammy. _____

2 The shopkeeper told us the shop was
   about to close. _____

3 Christine complained, "It's very cold in here." _____

4 The teacher told the class to put their
   books away. _____

4

Speech punctuation

These sentences contain direct speech. Add the missing speech marks.

1 The librarian explained, "The fiction books are over there.

2 Where have you been?" asked Daniel.

3 Tim asked, "Why were you late?

4 "How much does that cost?
   asked Andrew.

4

TOTAL MARKS 8

Nouns and pronouns

Common nouns

Common nouns name ordinary things.

book   pen   cat

Common nouns do not start with a capital letter, unless they are at the beginning of a sentence.

The rabbit hopped away.   Rabbits hopped around us.

Proper nouns

Proper nouns name people, places and things like the days of the week and the months of the year.

London   March   Annabel

Proper nouns begin with a capital letter, wherever they appear in a sentence.

Pronouns

Pronouns can sometimes be used in place of a noun.

I, she, me, him, we, them

They can save you from having to keep using the same noun again and again.

I couldn't find **Sam**.   I couldn't find **him**.

 The pronoun I is always a capital letter.

Key words   common noun   proper noun   pronoun   noun

Common nouns

Underline the common nouns in these sentences.

1 The cat was asleep.

2 Jonathon lost his bag.

3 Gran took an umbrella because it was raining.

3

Proper nouns

Circle the proper nouns in the box for one mark each.

Tuesday   box   house   Spain   guitar

Robert   wall   January   Friday   horse   fire

Cardiff   Worcester   desk   family   Barbara

8

Pronouns

Underline the pronoun in each sentence.

1 Mum asked George if he was hungry.

2 Jane and Kate ran for the bus, but they were too slow.

3 Luke stroked the cat, but it ran away.

3

TOTAL MARKS   14

Plurals

What is a plural?

Plural means more than one of something.

books

toys

bananas

Nouns are the only type of words that have **singular** and **plural** forms.

Writing plurals

With many nouns, you can just add an *s* to make the plural.

flower	flowers
chair	chairs
bird	birds

If the word ends in *ss, x, zz, sh* or *ch*, you must add *es* to make the plural.

cross	crosses
box	boxes
bush	bushes
church	churches

Try saying plurals out loud to help you to spell them. You can often hear the e in es plurals.

🔑 Key words   **singular plural**

What is a plural?

1 Write down your own definition for the word *plural* for one mark.

_____

2 Circle the plural words. You will get a mark for each one.

balls	dress	bush	schools
ink	bags	loss	wishes
eyes	table	mouse	horses

7

Writing plurals

Write down the plurals of these words.

1 kiss   _____

2 fox   _____

3 pencil   _____

4 fence   _____

5 wish   _____

6 ditch   _____

7 dog   _____

8 star   _____

8

Adjectives

What is an adjective?

Adjectives are words that describe nouns. They can help you to describe what colour, shape or size something is.

The car was red.

noun   adjective

The lawn was square.

I ordered a huge ice cream.

Choosing adjectives

Adjectives will make your writing more interesting to read, because your readers will find it easier to imagine what you are describing.

Some adjectives work harder than others. Try to avoid using boring adjectives like *big*, *small* or *nice*. Try to think of more interesting alternatives that say more about the thing you are describing.

big	enormous	huge	massive
small	tiny	minute	petite
nice	kind	thoughtful	friendly

Look out for strong adjectives when you are reading. Make a note of ones you could use in your own writing.

 Key words   adjective

What is an adjective?

Circle the adjectives in these sentences.

1 The Earth is round.

2 The cake was delicious.

3 Dad told us a funny joke.

4 Our teacher was happy because we finished our work.

5 The beautiful ballerina danced across the stage.

5

Choosing adjectives

Think of a better word to replace the red adjective in each sentence. Then write the sentence again, using your adjective.

1 A small spider had spun a web among the grass.

_____

_____

2 The bad boy stuck out his tongue.

_____

_____

3 I am reading a good book.

_____

_____

3

TOTAL MARKS 8

Verbs

Verbs are action words

Verbs are words that describe actions. They tell us what a person or thing is doing.

The rabbit is **eating**.   Eating is a verb.

The children **played**.   Played is a verb.

Using verbs

All sentences must contain a verb which tells us what the person or thing in the sentence is doing.

When you are writing, you have to choose the best verb to describe what the subject is doing.

The boy is **running**. The ball is **bouncing**.

Verb tenses

Verbs don't just tell us what is happening. They can tell us when it happens as well.

Verbs change tense to tell us whether something is happening now, has already happened, or will happen in the future.

I walked to school. (past tense)

I am walking to school. (present tense)

I shall walk to school. (future tense)

Lots of past tense verbs end in **ed**.

 Key words   tense   past tense   present tense   future tense

Verbs are action words

Underline the verb in each sentence.

1 The boy kicked the ball.

2 It rained all day.

3 The horse trotted around its field.

4 Our teacher collected the books.

5 The man hobbled down the street.

5

Using verbs

Pick the best verb from the box to complete each sentence.

swims   ate   helping   takes   planned

1 The girl _____ the cake.

2 A bus _____ us to school.

3 Our goldfish _____ around its bowl.

4 I love _____ Mum in the kitchen.

5 We _____ a big party for Dad's birthday.

5

Verb tenses

Circle the past tense verbs in these sentences.

1 We all laughed at Philip's joke.

2 The scouts cooked sausages on a campfire.

3 Our hamster climbed up the bars of its cage.

4 My class collected money for charity.

Top Tip *Don't forget, not all past tense verbs end in ed.*

5 I looked for my missing football boot.

5

TOTAL MARKS   15

Adverbs

How do adverbs work?

Adverbs are words we can use to describe verbs. They help us to say much more about what people or things are doing.

> The snowman melted **slowly**.

> The man shouted **loudly**.

Using adverbs is a quick and easy way to create a picture in your reader's mind.

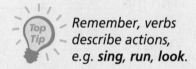
Top Tip — Remember, verbs describe actions, e.g. **sing, run, look**.

Adverbs and verbs

Verbs can tell us *what* a person or thing is doing, but they don't always tell us much about *how*. Adverbs can help you to build up a better picture for your reader by explaining how something is done.

Adverbs can change the meaning of a sentence, so you have to choose them carefully.

The girl walked briskly.

The girl walked slowly.

Key words   adverb

How do adverbs work?

Underline the adverbs in these sentences.

1 The plane climbed steadily.

2 Dad yawned sleepily.

3 The children waved cheerfully.

4 We crossed the road carefully.

5 Eve did her homework neatly.

5

Adverbs and verbs

Pick an adverb from the box to complete each sentence.

suddenly   quickly   politely   angrily   nervously

1 The boy shouted _____ at his younger brother.

2 Amy read her story _____ to the class.

3 Connor ran _____ to answer the door.

4 The girls asked _____ for a drink.

5 A bird swooped _____ over the garden.

5

TOTAL MARKS   10

Synonyms

What are synonyms?

Synonyms are words with similar meanings.

cold	➔	chilly
shoe	➔	boot
run	➔	jog
quickly	➔	rapidly

You can find lists of synonyms in a special book called a thesaurus.

Using synonyms

Synonyms help you to avoid having to use the same word again and again in your writing. This will make it more interesting to read.

My hair was **wet** and my clothes were **wet** through.

My hair was **soaked** and my clothes were **wet** through.

Read your writing carefully and, if you find that you keep using the same word, try to think of a different word you could use instead.

Key words   synonym   thesaurus

What are synonyms?

Match up the pairs of synonyms.

1 pretty   ocean

2 broken   jacket

3 walk   beautiful

4 coat   saunter

5 light   smashed

6 sea   lamp

6

Using synonyms

Write these sentences again, replacing one of the bold words with a suitable synonym from the box to avoid repetition.

> meadow   rushed   gloomy   broom

1 The **dark** corridor led into a **dark** courtyard.

_____

2 The cupboard held a dustpan and **brush** and a long-handled **brush**.

_____

_____

3 We walked across the **field** to a flowery **field**, where we ate our picnic.

_____

_____

4 I **hurried** out of the house and **hurried** to catch the bus.

_____

4

TOTAL MARKS 10

Imagery

Simile

Simile is a creative writing technique where one thing is compared to another using the words *as* or *like*. Similes are great for describing things and creating atmosphere in your stories.

> Helen shivered, her face as pale as a ghost.

There are lots of well-known similes, or you can make up your own to use in your writing.

Metaphor

Metaphor is another creative technique that can be used to describe things. With metaphor, a thing is described as if it really were something else.

> The moon was a lantern, lighting our way.

Personification

Personification works by describing non-human things using human characteristics.

> The flowers danced in the hedgerows.

Flowers do not really dance, but people do. Describing them as if they were dancing people helps the reader to picture how they were moving.

Techniques like simile, metaphor and personification are all types of imagery. This means that they help to build up a picture for your reader.

 Key words   simile   metaphor   personification   imagery

94

Simile

Underline the simile in each sentence.

1   Tom gobbled up his pizza like a pig.

2   Katie answered the door as fast as lightning.

3   The laundry fluttered on the line like bunting.

4   The kitten's fur was as soft as silk.

4

Metaphor

Put a tick next to the sentences that contain metaphors.

1   The night was a dark blanket across the landscape.

2   The cake was covered in pink icing, with four white candles.

3   The flower border was a rainbow, stretching down the garden.

4   The sky was deep blue, with fluffy white clouds.

4

Personification

Pick the correct word from each set of brackets, so that each sentence contains personification.

1   The moon (shone / smiled) down on us.

2   The branches of the trees (reached / stuck) out into the darkness.

3   Shadows (crept / moved) across the floor towards us.

4   A strong wind (chased / blew) dry autumn leaves off the trees.

4

TOTAL MARKS   12

Special effects

Alliteration

Thinking about how words sound can help you to write brilliant descriptions.

Start by thinking about the sound at the beginning of words. Grouping words that start with the same sound together can help to draw attention to important bits in your writing. This is called alliteration.

Snow White **bit** the **beautiful but bitter** apple.

Onomatopoeia

When you say some words, they sound like the noise they are describing. This is called onomatopoeia.

crackle

crunch

pop

screech

Be careful not to overdo creative techniques. Save them for parts of your writing that you want to draw your reader's attention to.

Key words   alliteration   onomatopoeia

Alliteration

Pick words from the box to complete each sentence.

winds	silver	towering	pound	ball

1 Billy bounced a blue _____.

2 Paul paid Peter a _____.

3 Sarah saw _____ stars sparkling.

4 Autumn leaves tumbled from _____ treetops.

5 Whistling _____ whipped wispy clouds.

5

Onomatopoeia

Match up each onomatopoeia with the correct picture.

1   shatter

2   drip

3   bang

4    fizz

5    sizzle

5

TOTAL MARKS   10

Instructions

What are instructions?

Instructions are non-fiction texts that tell you what to do.

There are lots of different types of instructions. Recipes and road signs are types of instructions, as are directions on how to do something. You will also find instructions on packaged foods, medicines and toiletries.

Instructions do not ask you to do something – they tell you how to do it!

Fix the hinge to part A.

Assemble parts B and C.

This is called the **imperative**. It is just a way of telling someone what to do.

Look in recipe or craft books to see how they use the imperative to tell the reader what to do.

Writing instructions

Instructions are often written as a numbered list, or as bullet points.

The task is broken down into small steps for the reader to follow. You must list them in the correct order or the user will not get the result they need! The steps are often numbered, to make sure that they are carried out in the correct order.

Remember to give your instructions a title too, so your reader knows what the outcome of following them will be.

 Key words   instructions   imperative

What are instructions?

Underline the imperatives in these instructions.

How to make crispy cakes

1 Melt the chocolate over a low heat.

2 Add the crisp rice cereal.

3 Stir until the cereal is coated with the melted chocolate.

4 Spoon the mixture into paper cake cases.

5 Refrigerate until set.

5

Writing instructions

Number the steps 1–5 to put these instructions into the correct order.

How to wash your hair

Work shampoo into a lather. ☐

Wet hair thoroughly. ☐

Dry hair. ☐

Apply shampoo. ☐

Rinse thoroughly. ☐

Top Tip *Thinking about how you would actually do a task can help you to put the steps into the correct order.*

5

TOTAL MARKS ☐ 10

Persuasive writing

Types of persuasive writing

The aim of **persuasive writing** is to convince the reader to adopt a particular point of view, or to buy a product or visit an attraction.

There are lots of different types of persuasive writing. We are surrounded by it all the time. Adverts on the TV, radio and Internet, and in magazines and newspapers, are all persuasive writing. So are many leaflets and posters.

The language of persuasion

Persuasive writing often contains very few words, so each one is very important. Good writers use lots of powerful adjectives to make whatever they are writing about sound really exciting.

Hill Heights is *fantastic*. The *most exciting* place to visit this weekend!

Keep your language simple, so that everyone will understand it, especially if you are writing for children. Think about what would persuade you to try the product or attraction yourself. Give reasons why it is a good product or place to visit.

 Have a look at adverts, leaflets and posters and think about how they have used language to persuade their readers.

 Key words | persuasive writing

Types of persuasive writing

Circle the phrases that describe a type of persuasive writing.

a recipe

a postcard

a magazine advert

a road map

a diary

a poster advertising a film

a holiday brochure

a leaflet about a new leisure centre

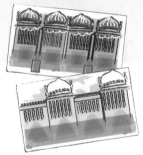

4

The language of persuasion

Read these sentences about a new film.

a Space Battles is a film with lots of special effects, starring lots of famous actors.

b Space Battles is an exciting film packed with incredible special effects and starring the biggest names in Hollywood.

1 Put a tick in the box beside the sentence you find more persuasive.

2 Underline the powerful adjectives in the sentence you choose.

3 Which sentence has more powerful adjectives?

a   **b**

3

Recounts

What is a recount?

Recounts tell readers about something that has happened.

A recount could be an account of a holiday, a funny story about something that happened to you, or a piece of biographical writing.

> We had a lovely time at the beach yesterday. We built a sandcastle and went in the sea before lunch. After we had eaten we hired a motorboat. In the evening we went out for dinner.
> Sam

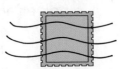

Chris Black
Tall Trees
Home Town
UK

Writing a recount

Recounts are non-fiction writing, so they tend not to include a lot of imagery, like similes, metaphors and personification.

Because they are about an event that has already happened, recounts are written in the past tense. The events are described in the order in which they happened and they are often linked together with time connectives like *after that, suddenly* and *all at once*.

> *At first* I did not realise that my bag had gone. *As soon as* I noticed, I went to the lost property office. They took my name and a description of the bag. *By the time* I got home, my bag had been handed in.

 Try using a time line to plan your recount. It will help to ensure you get events in the right order and don't miss anything out.

 Key words | recount   time connective

What is a recount?

Write down three different types of recounts.

1 _____

_____

2 _____

_____

3 _____

_____

3

Writing a recount

Underline five time connectives in this recount.

We went to the animal rescue centre to adopt a pet cat.

First we looked at some kittens and then an old black cat.

After that we saw a lovely tabby with white paws, followed by

a black fluffy cat. Finally we chose a beautiful tortoiseshell

cat called Tigger.

5

TOTAL MARKS 8

Reports

What are reports for?

A report is an information text about a particular subject. Reports can be about almost any topic, so you will probably have to write them in other classes as well as English.

Reports are organised into topics, rather than chronologically, and they are often written in the present tense.

The UK buries millions of tons of rubbish in landfill sites each year. Much of this could be recycled.

Planning reports

The information in reports is organised into topics, but that can be harder than it sounds!

Start by researching your topic in books and on the Internet. Decide which bits of information you want to use, then plan it on paper to find a logical way to present the information. Try using a spidergram to organise your ideas. It will help you to group your ideas into topics and ensure that you don't miss anything out when you come to write the report.

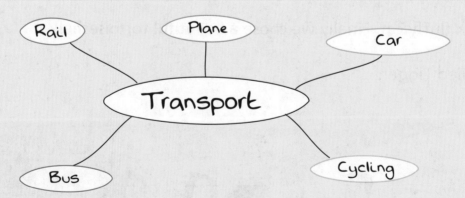

Rail   Plane   Car
Transport
Bus   Cycling

Once you have a spidergram, you can simply write one paragraph for each section of your plan.

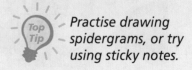

Top Tip — *Practise drawing spidergrams, or try using sticky notes.*

Key words   report   spidergram

What are reports for?

Which of these things are reports? Underline your choices.

1 An advert for a new film.

2 Writing about woodland and the animals that live there.

3 A project on the Tudors.

4 A story about a magic lantern.

Chembakolli

5 A piece of text about a village in India.

6 A recipe for blueberry muffins.

3

Planning reports

Here is a spidergram for a report about the sports on offer at a school. Colour in the six ideas on this spidergram, so that they match the key. You will get one mark for each.

Key: red = ball games   blue = athletics

Add one more idea for each topic and colour it to match the others, for two further marks.

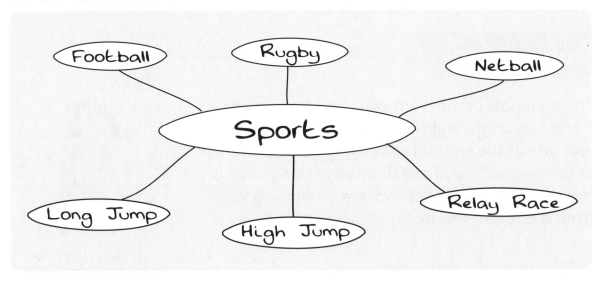

 Top Tip *Using colours is a great way to sort your ideas into topics.*

8

TOTAL MARKS 11

Planning stories

Story openings

Writing stories can be daunting, but you can make it much easier if you spend time planning the story before you start. You need to decide how it will start, what will happen in the middle and how it will end.

A story opening is your first chance to hook your reader. Try to start the action straight away and leave a question unanswered in the first few sentences. That way, the reader has to keep reading to find out what happens next.

Get off to a great start by using lots of strong descriptive words in your opening.

What happens next?

You need to think carefully about what happens to your characters in the story. It is a good idea if they have to face some sort of problem or difficulty. Then you can write about how they overcome it.

Make sure you keep the action going in the middle of the story. It is very easy to start long, rambling descriptions that don't actually keep the plot moving along.

Story endings

There are lots of different ways you can end your story. You might want your characters to be happy and safe at the end of the story, or to be punished in some way if they have done something wrong. Your ending must follow on in a convincing way from the rest of the story.

 Really good endings give the reader something to think about after they have finished the story.

Story openings

Read this story. It leaves a question unanswered.

> The house on Sycamore Lane had been empty for years. Now there was movement once more behind the grimy net curtains and smoke curling out of the chimney. Strange, purplish smoke. Nobody seemed to know who had moved in.

Tick the unanswered question.

Is the house on fire? ☐   Who is living in the house? ☐

Why doesn't anyone know who has moved in? ☐

1

What happens next?

Reread the story opening above. Imagine you are a character living in the house next door and you decide to find out who is living in the house. Write down two ideas for problems or difficulties you might face in your quest to find out about your new neighbours.

1 _____

_____

2 _____

_____

2

Story endings

Choose your favourite plot idea from the previous section, then think about how your story could end. Write a sentence to say what would happen.

_____

_____

1

TOTAL MARKS 4

Characters and settings

Developing characters

Characters are the people in your stories. They are the most important part of a story, because readers don't want to read about boring characters.

Don't try to cram too many characters into your stories. It is better to have two or three that you can describe really well and bring them to life.

Think carefully about what each character is like before you start writing. Don't just imagine what they look like. Think about how they behave and what they say too.

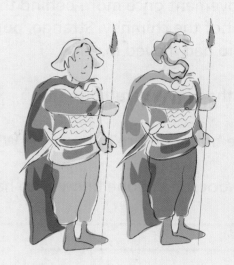

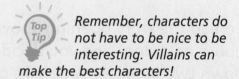

Remember, characters do not have to be nice to be interesting. Villains can make the best characters!

Writing about settings

The setting is the place where the story happens. Describing the setting can be a brilliant way to create the right atmosphere in your story. For example, a science fiction story could have a space-age setting and a ghost story could be set in a haunted house.

Using imagery like simile, metaphor and personification will help you to create really convincing settings.

> The old house crouched in the moonlight, like a troll.

Developing characters

Imagine you are writing a story about a boy who finds some valuable Roman treasure in his garden. The boy's mean neighbour decides to dig up the boy's garden at night to try to find some more. Choose either the boy or the neighbour, then write a character profile.

1 Name: _____

2 Age: _____

3 Personality:

☐ greedy   ☐ brave

☐ honest   ☐ dishonest

4 Appearance: _____

5 How does he feel about the treasure? _____

6 Descriptive word or phrase to describe how he moves:

_____

> **Top Tip** *Having two characters that are complete opposites can work really well. Think about the story of Beauty and the Beast!*

6

Writing about settings

The neighbour is about to dig up the boy's garden in the middle of the night. Think of powerful words or phrases to complete these sentences about the garden setting.

1 The neighbour squeezed through a gap in the _____ hedge.

2 Moonlight spread across the garden like _____.

3 Silent trees _____ the man as he began to dig.

3

TOTAL MARKS   9

Poetry

What is poetry?

A lot of people find poetry scary, but there is no need to. It can be great fun!

A poem is a type of text that uses rhythm or **rhyme** to show an idea in a vivid way, along with powerful vocabulary. Lots of poems have rhyming words at the end of each line, but they don't have to.

Most poems contain far fewer words than you would find in a story, so every word has to work really hard. Poets often use alliteration, onomatopoeia and personification to add to the effect.

Read as many different types of poems as you can, to give you a better idea of how the different types work.

Writing list poems

Writing poetry doesn't need to be difficult! A **list poem** is simply a list of powerful descriptions, based on the same subject. The descriptions in the list don't need to rhyme and each one is self-contained, so you can use a different creative technique for each one if you want to.

Sweet is...

jolly jellies, jiving, ← alliteration

crunchy crispy cakes, ← personification

ripe cherries, like jewels, ← alliteration and onomatopoeia

pink candy floss clouds. ← simile

metaphor

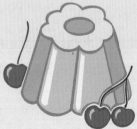

🔑 **Key words**   rhyme   list poem

What is poetry?

Pick words from the box to complete this piece of writing about poetry.

rhyme　　words　　personification　　rhythm　　poet

The person who writes a poem is called a _____.

Poems use _____ or rhyme to help show an idea in a

powerful way. Poems have fewer _____ than a story,

so each one has to work really hard. Most poems contain creative

techniques like alliteration, onomatopoeia and _____.

Not all poems have to _____, but some do.

5

Writing list poems

Add five lines to complete
this list poem.

Hot is...

_____

The smiling sun,

_____

Steaming mugs of cocoa,

_____

_____

_____

_____

_____

5

TOTAL MARKS 　 10

Glossary

adjective a word or phrase that describes a noun

adverb a word or phrase that describes a verb

alliteration a phrase where most or all of the words begin with the same sound

apostrophe a punctuation mark used for contraction when two words are joined, e.g. he'll, or to show possession, e.g. We'll collect Dad's car.

author the person who writes a text

autobiography the story of someone's life that they write themselves

biography the story of someone's life written by someone else

blurb information on the back of a book designed to give the reader an idea of what it is about

character the people or animals that a story is about

clause a distinct part of a sentence including a verb

comma a punctuation mark that shows when to pause, separates clauses or separates items in a list

common noun a noun that names ordinary things, e.g. book, car

comprehension understanding what a text is about

contraction when words are shortened, or two words are joined, by removing letters and replacing with an apostrophe, e.g. can't, won't

curriculum vitae a summary of a person's experience and qualifications

dialogue a spoken or written conversation between two people

direct speech words that are actually spoken, enclosed in speech marks

exclamation mark a punctuation mark that can be used instead of a full stop to indicate surprise or that an order has been made, e.g. Ouch!

fact a piece of information that can be tested and proven to be true

fiction stories with imaginary characters, settings or events

future tense describes things that will happen in the future

glossary a collection of useful words and their meanings

imagery words used to build up a picture in a story, including simile, metaphor and personification

imperative a way of using verbs to give an order or instruction, e.g. Turn left at the traffic lights.

index an alphabetical list of the topics in a book

instructions texts that tell people what to do, or how to do something, e.g. recipes

ISBN a unique number on the back of a book used by booksellers and libraries

list poem a poem that consists of a list of descriptions based on a single theme

metaphor where a writer describes something as if it were something else, e.g. The bird was an arrow, tearing across the sky.

narrator the person from whose viewpoint a story is told, who may or may not be a character in the story

non-fiction writing that is not fictional, including information texts about real people and places, letters, instructions and reports

noun a word that names a thing or feeling

onomatopoeia where a word sounds like the noise it describes, e.g. crash, shatter

past tense describes things that have already happened

personification a writing technique in which human characteristics are used to describe non-human things, e.g. Shadows crept across the floor.

persuasive writing writing that aims to persuade the reader to adopt a particular viewpoint, or buy a product or service, e.g. magazine adverts, posters, leaflets

plural more than one of something, usually made by adding s or es, e.g. dogs, dresses

possessive apostrophe an apostrophe used to show that something belongs to someone, e.g. Sarah's homework

present tense describes things that are happening now

pronoun a word used instead of a noun to avoid having to use the same noun again, e.g. I, she, we, me

proper noun a noun that names a specific person, thing or place, e.g. Chris, Manchester, Friday

punctuation marks used to make writing clear, e.g. .,!?"

question mark a punctuation mark used in place of a full stop to show that a question is being asked

recount a report that describes events in chronological order or the order in which they happened

report an information text about a particular subject

reported speech speech reported in a text, but not directly quoted, e.g. She said she was tired.

rhyme an effect created when endings of a pair or group of words sound the same, e.g. rabbit, habit

scanning reading quickly to find a specific piece of information

sentence a unit of text that makes sense on its own

simile where a writer compares one thing with another, using the words as or like, e.g. as bold as brass

simple sentence a sentence containing one clause

singular one of something, e.g. a bird

skimming reading quickly to understand the main meaning of a piece of text

speaking and listening the skill of being able to listen to ideas and comment on them

speech marks punctuation marks that surround direct speech. Other punctuation goes inside them, e.g. "Goodbye," said Mum.

spidergram a diagram that can help writers to organise their ideas before writing reports and recounts

subject the person or thing in a sentence that carries out the action, e.g. Amy bit the apple.

synonym a word with exactly or nearly the same meaning as another word, e.g. hot, warm

tense tells us when something is happening

thesaurus a book of synonyms

time connective a word or phrase that connects different parts of a text to show when things happened

verb a doing or being word, e.g. walk, sleep

PAGE 7
Answering problems
1. 30g
2. 7 years old
3. 19km
4. 240
5. £171
6. 54cm

Multi-step problems
1. 33
2. 20
3. 4 sweets in a bag and 7 left over
4. £8.75

PAGE 9
Reasoning
1. 27 years older
   36 – 9
2. 17
3. 33
4.
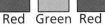
Red Green Red

Yellow Blue Orange

Finding all possibilities
1. 1 and 15, 3 and 13, 5 and 11, 7 and 9
2. 4 hot-dogs and 5 burgers
3. 4 20p stickers and 12 10p stickers

PAGE 11
Number sequences
1. 47, 48, **49**, **50**, 51, 52, **53**
2. 163, **164**, 165, **166**, 167, **168**, 169
3. **81**, **80**, 79, 78, **77**, 76, 75
4. 297, 298, 299, **300**, **301**, **302**, 303
5. 402, 401, **400**, **399**, 398, 397, **396**

Number patterns
1. **39**, **45**, 51, 57, 63, **69**, **75**
2. **18**, **25**, 32, 39, 46, **53**, **60**
3. **48**, **44**, 40, 36, 32, **28**, **24**
4. **71**, **76**, 81, 86, 91, **96**, **101**

Function machines
1. 7
2. 57
3. 33
4. 7

PAGE 13
4-digit numbers
1. 9642
2. 425
3. 3213
4. 1598
5. 6070
6. 2058
7. 8360
8. 7009

Decimal numbers
1. 7.1
2. 7.5
3. 8.2
4. 8.8
5. 3.4
6. 3.7
7. 4.3
8. 4.9

PAGE 15
Comparing numbers
1. 56 < 93
2. 87 > 78
3. 44 > 42
4. 19 < 61
5. 53 > 35
6. 220 < 310
7. 964 > 938
8. 572 < 575
9. 414 > 141
10. 883 > 838

Ordering numbers
1. 198, 258, 296, 385
2. 527, 572, 592, 597
3. 1043, 3014, 4130, 4301
4. 2556, 2566, 2656, 2665
5. 248, 294, 367, 712
6. 393, 399, 3939, 9339

PAGE 17
Rounding
1. 60
2. 70
3. 40
4. 60
5. 910
6. 430
7. 800
8. 150

Approximate answers
1. 80
2. 50
3. 150
4. 70
5. 30
6. 60
7. 140
8. 160

PAGE 19
Types of fractions

	$\frac{7}{3}$	$4\frac{2}{5}$	$\frac{10}{9}$	$\frac{4}{5}$	$\frac{3}{7}$	$3\frac{2}{3}$	$\frac{5}{2}$
Proper fraction				✔	✔		
Improper fraction	✔		✔				✔
Mixed number		✔				✔	

Parts of a fraction
1. $\frac{1}{5}$
2. $\frac{1}{12}$
3. $\frac{5}{6}$
4. $\frac{4}{7}$
5. $\frac{3}{10}$
6. $\frac{7}{9}$

Equivalent fractions
1. $\frac{1}{2}$ and $\frac{3}{6}$
2. $\frac{1}{4}$ and $\frac{2}{8}$
3. $\frac{2}{6}$ and $\frac{1}{3}$
4. $\frac{2}{20}$ and $\frac{1}{10}$
5. $\frac{1}{3}$ and $\frac{3}{9}$

PAGE 21
Number facts

1	11	6	20
2	8	7	70
3	15	8	10
4	13	9	80
5	17	10	50

Trios

1	9	4	10
2	4	5	6
3	10	6	6

PAGE 23
Times tables

1	14	6	27
2	20	7	28
3	18	8	16
4	16	9	30
5	45	10	70

Multiples

1	50 and 20	4	15
2	50, 8, 14 and 20	5	8 and 14
3	50, 15 and 20	6	15 and 9

PAGE 25
Dividing

1	4	5	8
2	8	6	6
3	7	7	9
4	9	8	14g

Missing number problems

1	7	5	6
2	8	6	14
3	5	7	5
4	9	8	6

PAGE 27
Adding 2-digit numbers

1   37 → c
    75 → a
    58 → t   3   49 → g
2   63 → d   81 → o
    81 → o   75 → a
    49 → g   58 → t
                   4   58 → t
                      81 → o
                      75 → a
                      63 → d

Counting on

1	23	4	21
2	45	5	23
3	32	6	57

PAGE 29
Written method for adding

1	665	3	700
2	790	4	423
5	901	7	802
6	642	8	903

Adding money

1	£4.99	5	£2.34
2	£2.18	6	£1.76
3	£4.15	7	£4.49
4	£1.97	8	£2.72

PAGE 31
Column method

1	338	6	456
2	20	7	239
3	388	8	244
4	608	9	339
5	203		

Number line method

1	45	3	185
2	20	4	173

PAGE 33
Mental calculations

×	14	19	17
5	70	95	85
3	42	57	51

Written methods

1   112
2   324
3

120	27

120 + 27 = 147

4

350	15

350 + 15 = 365

5	74	8	220
6	285	9	252
7	172	10	171

PAGE 35
Doubling and halving

1	18	5	43
2	32	6	13
3	74	7	29
4	90	8	24

Division and remainders

1	22r2	5	47
2	19r3	6	4
3	22r3	7	4
4	17r1		

PAGE 37
Fractions of shapes

1	$\frac{1}{2}$	4	$\frac{1}{4}$
2	$\frac{1}{3}$	5	$\frac{1}{4}$
3	$\frac{1}{5}$	6	$\frac{1}{2}$

Fractions and division

1 4	6 12
2 4	7 4
3 7	8 8
4 2	9 3
5 6	

PAGE 39
Lines of symmetry

1

5

2

6 Either of these lines of symmetry

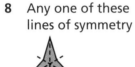

3

4 Any one of these lines of symmetry

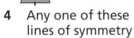

7

8 Any one of these lines of symmetry

Reflections

1

3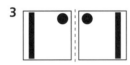

2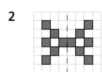

4

PAGE 41
Polygons

1 6 sides – hexagon	4 5 sides – pentagon
2 6 sides – hexagon	5 8 sides – octagon
3 3 sides – triangle	6 7 sides – heptagon

Regular polygons

Shape	Property of shape		
	4 sides	A regular shape	1 or more right angles
▭	✔	✗	✔
⬡	✗	✔	✗
⬠	✗	✗	✔
▯	✔	✔	✔
△	✗	✔	✗

PAGE 43
Names of 3D shapes

1 cylinder	5 triangular prism
2 sphere	6 cuboid
3 cube	7 cone
4 cylinder	8 cuboid

Parts of solid shapes

1 4	3 tetrahedron
2 cube	4 sphere

PAGE 45
Right angles

1

5

2

6

3

7

4

8

Types of angles

1 c	5 a
2 b	6 c and d
3 a	7 b
4 e	8 b

PAGE 47
Coordinates

1   (1,2)   2   (2,4)   3   (4,8)

4

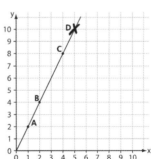

Points of the compass
1 & 2

Directions

1 South	3 South-East
2 West	

PAGE 49
Units of measure
1 14cm
2 2 litre
3 2m
4 60g
5 3km

Converting units
1 4000ml
2 5500m
3 700cm
4 3500g
5 120mm

Reading scales
1 2cm
2 25mm

PAGE 51
Finding perimeters
1 124m
2 5m
3 11cm
4 7cm

Finding areas
1 4 square cm
2 7 square cm
3 9 square cm
4 6 square cm

PAGE 53
Time facts
1 28 days
2 90 minutes
3 Monday
4 36 months
5 1 day
6 30th April

Telling the time
1
2
3 (clock)
4
5
6

PAGE 55
Bar charts
1 90 km/h
2 Hare
3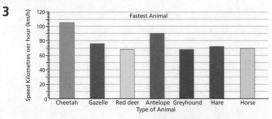
4 Antelope

Pictograms
1 Tuesday
2 4
3 Thursday
4 11
5 3

PAGE 57
Venn diagrams

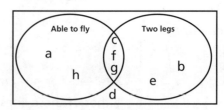

Carroll diagrams

	1 or more right angles	No right angles
Quadrilateral	c, d	f, h
Not a quadrilateral	b, e	a, g

PAGE 61
Taking turns
Answers will vary, but one mark should be awarded for each point noted.

Getting ready to speak
Answers will vary, but one mark should be awarded for each point noted.

PAGE 63
On the cover
Answers will vary, but one mark should be awarded for each of the following features on the cover: title, cover illustration, name of author.

Inside books
1 front
2 alphabetically
3 glossary
4 back
5 back

PAGE 65
What is fiction?
Fiction: The Christmas Pony, Nasty Nigel, Martin's Mountain
Non-fiction: Cricket, Scotland

What is non-fiction?
Answers will vary, but one mark should be given for stating a preference between fiction and non-fiction, and one mark for writing a sentence explaining the preference.

PAGE 67
Skimming
1 a family holiday
2 a girl
3 fiction

Scanning
1 10 years old
2 Max
3 Florida

PAGE 69
What is an author?
1 An author is a person who writes a text.
2 non-fiction
3 To arrange books alphabetically.

What is a narrator?
1 Sentences will vary, but might include: A narrator is the storyteller in a piece of fiction.
2 yes

PAGE 71
Biography
Biography: 1, 3
Autobiography: 2, 4, 5

Autobiography
Answers will vary, but one mark should be awarded for each of the following features: writer's birthplace, current home, family, friends and school.

PAGE 73
Rules for sentences
1 Stop that dreadful noise.
2 Where is my coat?
3 The bus was late, so we missed the start of the film
4 We are going to France on holiday.
5 It was my birthday on Friday.

Clauses
True: 1, 3, 5
False: 2, 4

PAGE 75
How contractions work
1 he's
2 we'll
3 she'd
4 couldn't
5 she'll

Writing contracted forms
1 you'll
2 you've
3 we're
4 I'd
5 shouldn't

PAGE 77
Using possessive apostrophes
1 Dawn's shoes were too small.
2 I found the dog's lead and took him for a walk.
3 My sister's room is bigger than mine.
4 Tim's birthday is next Friday.
5 A duck's feathers keep it warm and dry.

Possessive apostrophes for groups
1 boys'
2 friends'
3 shops'
4 cars'
5 cats'

PAGE 79

What is punctuation for?

1 Greg ran down the stairs two at a time and bounded through the kitchen, grabbing a piece of toast on the way.

2 "Where are you off to?" asked Dad.

3 "I'm late for school!" panted Greg.

4 Dad laughed, "Greg, it's Saturday!"

Ending sentences

1 What time is it?

2 We went to the theatre on Saturday.

3 I don't believe it!

4 How are you feeling?

Commas

1 I need to buy pencils, a ruler and a sharpener for school.

2 Alex, James, Jack and Ali got parts in the school play.

3 I packed pyjamas, slippers, a toothbrush and toothpaste for the sleepover party.

4 We made a fruit smoothie with bananas, strawberries, raspberries and pears.

PAGE 81

Direct and reported speech

Direct speech: 1, 3

Reported speech: 2, 4

Speech punctuation

1 The librarian explained, "The fiction books are over there."

2 "Where have you been?" asked Daniel.

3 Tim asked, "Why were you late?"

4 "How much does that cost?" asked Andrew.

PAGE 83

Common nouns

1 The cat was asleep.

2 Jonathon lost his bag.

3 Gran took an umbrella because it was raining.

Proper nouns

The proper nouns are: Tuesday, Spain, Robert, January, Friday, Cardiff, Worcester, Barbara.

Pronouns

1 Mum asked George if he was hungry.

2 Jane and Kate ran for the bus, but they were too slow.

3 Luke stroked the cat, but it ran away.

PAGE 85

What is a plural?

1 Answers will vary, but might include: A plural means more than one of something.

2 The plurals are: balls, eyes, bags, schools, wishes, horses.

Writing plurals

1 kisses

2 foxes

3 pencils

4 fences

5 wishes

6 ditches

7 dogs

8 stars

PAGE 87

What is an adjective?

1 The Earth is round.

2 The cake was delicious.

3 Dad told us a funny joke.

4 Our teacher was happy because we finished our work.

5 The beautiful ballerina danced across the stage.

Choosing adjectives

Answers will vary, but might include:

1 A tiny spider had spun a web among the grass.

2 The naughty boy stuck out his tongue.

3 I am reading a brilliant book.

PAGE 89

Verbs are action words

1 The boy kicked the ball.

2 It rained all day.

3 The horse trotted around its field.

4 Our teacher collected the books.

5 The man hobbled down the street.

Using verbs

1 The girl ate the cake.

2 A bus takes us to school.

3 Our goldfish swims around its bowl.

4 I love helping Mum in the kitchen.

5 We planned a big party for Dad's birthday.

Verb tenses

1 We all laughed at Philip's joke.

2 The scouts cooked sausages on a campfire.

3 Our hamster climbed up the bars of its cage.

4 My class collected money for charity.

5 I looked for my missing football boot.

PAGE 91

How do adverbs work?
1 The plane climbed <u>steadily</u>.
2 Dad yawned <u>sleepily</u>.
3 The children waved <u>cheerfully</u>.
4 We crossed the road <u>carefully</u>.
5 Eve did her homework <u>neatly</u>.

Adverbs and verbs
1 The boy shouted angrily at his younger brother.
2 Amy read her story nervously to the class.
3 Connor ran quickly to answer the door.
4 The girls asked politely for a drink.
5 A bird swooped suddenly over the garden.

PAGE 93

What are synonyms?

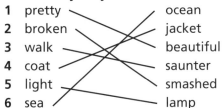

1 pretty
2 broken
3 walk
4 coat
5 light
6 sea

ocean
jacket
beautiful
saunter
smashed
lamp

Using synonyms
Answers may vary, but might include:
1 The dark corridor led into a gloomy courtyard.
2 The cupboard held a dustpan and brush and a long-handled broom.
3 We walked across the field to a flowery meadow, where we ate our picnic.
4 I rushed out of the house and hurried to catch the bus.

PAGE 95

Simile
1 Tom gobbled up his pizza <u>like a pig</u>.
2 Katie answered the door <u>as fast as lightning</u>.
3 The laundry fluttered on the line <u>like bunting</u>.
4 The kitten's fur was <u>as soft as silk</u>.

Metaphor
Sentences 1 and 3 contain metaphors.

Personification
1 The moon smiled down on us.
2 The branches of the trees reached out into the darkness.
3 Shadows crept across the floor towards us.
4 A strong wind chased dry autumn leaves off the trees.

PAGE 97

Alliteration
1 Billy bounced a blue ball.
2 Paul paid Peter a pound.
3 Sarah saw silver stars sparkling.
4 Autumn leaves tumbled from towering treetops.
5 Whistling winds whipped wispy clouds.

Onomatopoeia

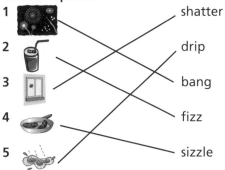

1 shatter
2 drip
3 bang
4 fizz
5 sizzle

PAGE 99

What are instructions?
1 <u>Melt</u> the chocolate over a low heat.
2 <u>Add</u> the crisp rice cereal.
3 <u>Stir</u> until the cereal is coated with the melted chocolate.
4 <u>Spoon</u> the mixture into paper cake cases.
5 <u>Refrigerate</u> until set.

Writing instructions
1 Wet hair thoroughly.
2 Apply shampoo.
3 Work shampoo into a lather.
4 Rinse thoroughly.
5 Dry hair.

PAGE 101

Types of persuasive writing
The following are types of persuasive writing: a magazine advert, a poster advertising a film, a leaflet about a new leisure centre, a holiday brochure.

The language of persuasion
1 Sentence b) is more persuasive.
2 Space Battles is an <u>exciting</u> film packed with <u>incredible</u> special effects and starring the <u>biggest</u> names in Hollywood.
3 Sentence b) has more powerful adjectives.

PAGE 103

What is a recount?
Answers will vary, but might include:
1 a biography
2 an account of a school trip
3 a story about something funny that happened

Writing a recount
We went to the animal rescue centre to adopt a pet cat. <u>First</u> we looked at some kittens and <u>then</u> an old black cat. <u>After that</u> we saw a lovely tabby with white paws, <u>followed</u> by a black fluffy cat. <u>Finally</u> we chose a beautiful tortoiseshell cat called Tigger.

PAGE 105

What are reports for?
The following are reports: 2, 3, 5

Planning reports
Football, rugby and netball should be coloured red. Long jump, high jump and relay race should be coloured blue.
Sports added will vary, but should be coloured according to the key.

PAGE 107

Story openings
The unanswered question is:
Who is living in the house?

What happens next?
Answers will vary, but might include:
1 You are peering through the net curtains during the day, when they suddenly open and a face looks back at you.
2 You creep inside the house and the door slams shut behind you, trapping you inside.

Story endings
Answers will vary, but might include:
You discover that a scientist has bought the house. She has a daughter your age and you become friends.

PAGE 109

Developing characters
Answers will vary, but one mark should be awarded for each character development.

Writing about settings
Answers will vary, but might include:
1 The neighbour squeezed through a gap in the prickly hedge.
2 Moonlight spread across the garden like fingers.
3 Silent trees watched the man as he began to dig.

PAGE 111

What is poetry?
The person who writes a poem is called a poet. Poems use rhythm or rhyme to help show an idea in a powerful way. Poems have fewer words than a story, so each one has to work really hard. Most poems contain creative techniques like alliteration, onomatopoeia and personification. Not all poems have to rhyme, but some do.

Writing list poems
Answers will vary, but might include:
Hot is...
The smiling sun,
Steaming mugs of cocoa,
Red-hot chilli peppers
A piping jacuzzi,
Yummy Indian curry,
Sizzling steaks on a barbecue,
Toasty hot water bottle.

Letts Educational, an imprint of HarperCollinsPublishers
77–85 Fulham Palace Road
London W6 8JB

Telephone: 0844 576 8126
Fax: 0844 576 8131
Email: education@harpercollins.co.uk
Website: www.lettsrevision.com

ISBN 9781844196951

Text © Paul Broadbent and Alison Head

Design and illustration © 2008 Letts Educational, an imprint of HarperCollinsPublishers

This edition first published 2012